About this book

This Workbook is written to support and consolidate understanc of the key ideas contained in the accompanying Student Book: *Framework Maths 7A.*

The Student Book contains units of work, each of which is broken down into spreads of content designed to last approximately one hour.

This Workbook contains 76 worksheets of extra material that can be used alongside the Student Book spreads, for example A1.1 WS is designed to be used alongside spread A1.1.

Not every spread has an accompanying worksheet, but the main concepts you need to understand from the course are covered so you can use the Workbook as a record of your achievement.

The worksheets are self-contained so they can be used for homework.

The start of each unit can be found on these pages:

1 Continue these patterns.

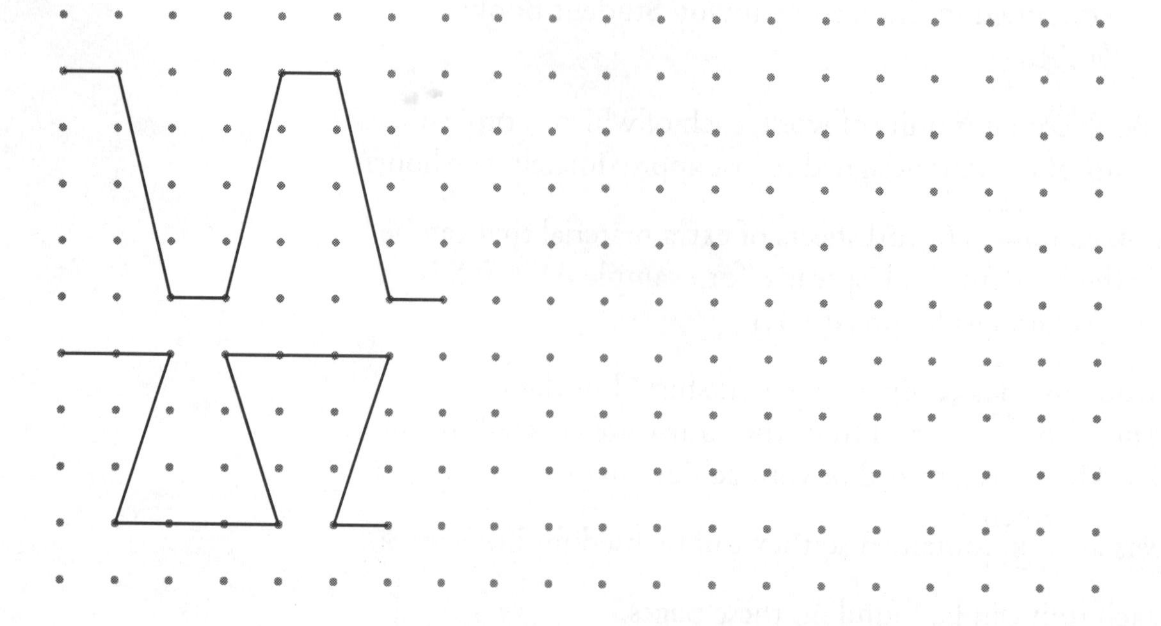

2 Use three colours to make a repeating pattern on these beads.

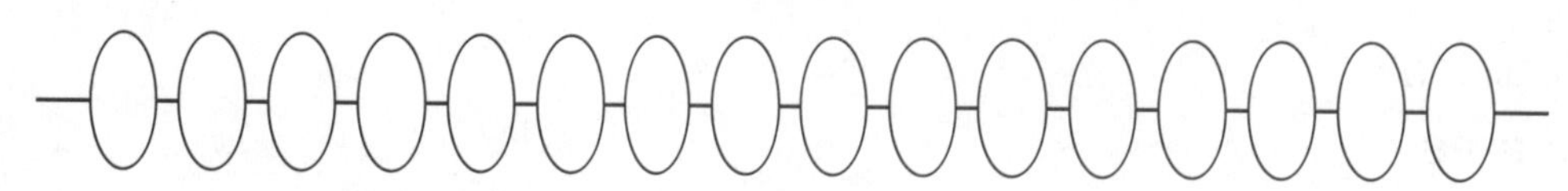

3 Here is a pattern that grows. Complete the last two parts of this pattern.

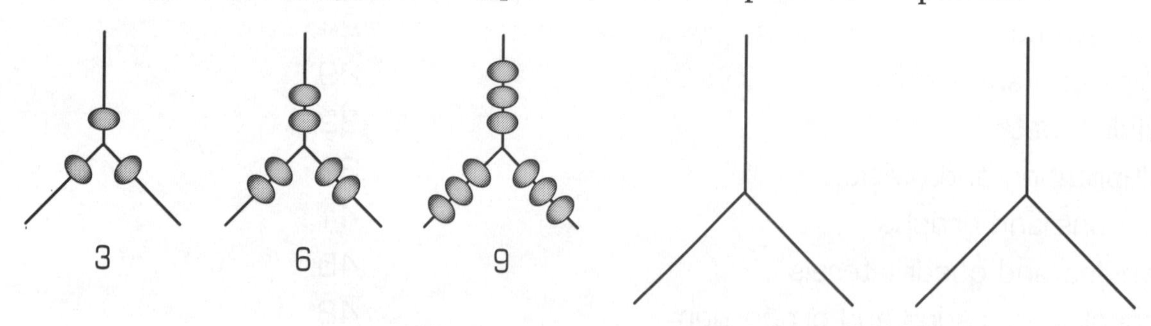

4 Each set of cards shows a number pattern.
Complete the pattern.

a 2 | 4 | 6 | 8 | ___ | ___

b 5 | 10 | 15 | 20 | ___ | ___

A1.2WS Introducing sequences

1 Write the next number in each sequence in the box.

a

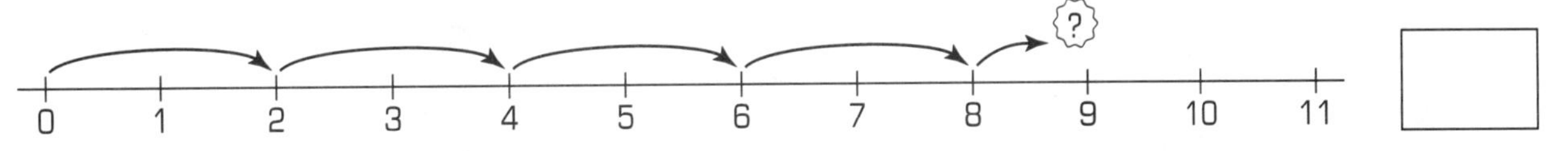

b

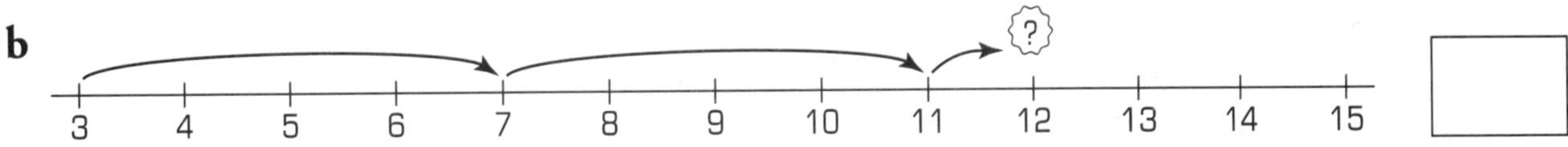

c

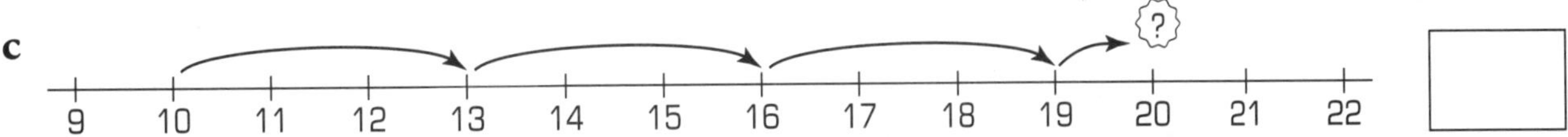

2 Complete each sequence and explain the pattern.
Here are some words to help you.

> This sequence increases by ____ each time.
> This sequence decreases by ____ each time.
> This sequence is in the ____ times table.

a 1 , 4 , 7 , 10 , ___ , ___ This sequence ______________________________

b 10 , 20 , 30 , 40 , ___ , ___ This sequence ______________________________

c 0 , 4 , 8 , 12 , ___ , ___ This sequence ______________________________

d 3 , 8 , 13 , 18 , ___ , ___ This sequence ______________________________

e 24 , 21 , 18 , 15 , ___ , ___ This sequence ______________________________

3 Use the rule to write the first five numbers in each sequence.

a The first number is 0. The rule is +3. ___ , ___ , ___ , ___ , ___

b The first number is 2. The rule is +2. ___ , ___ , ___ , ___ , ___

c The first number is 7. The rule is +5. ___ , ___ , ___ , ___ , ___

d The first number is 19. The rule is −3. ___ , ___ , ___ , ___ , ___

Sequences and rules

1 Start at the bottom and follow the sequence to work out who is who!

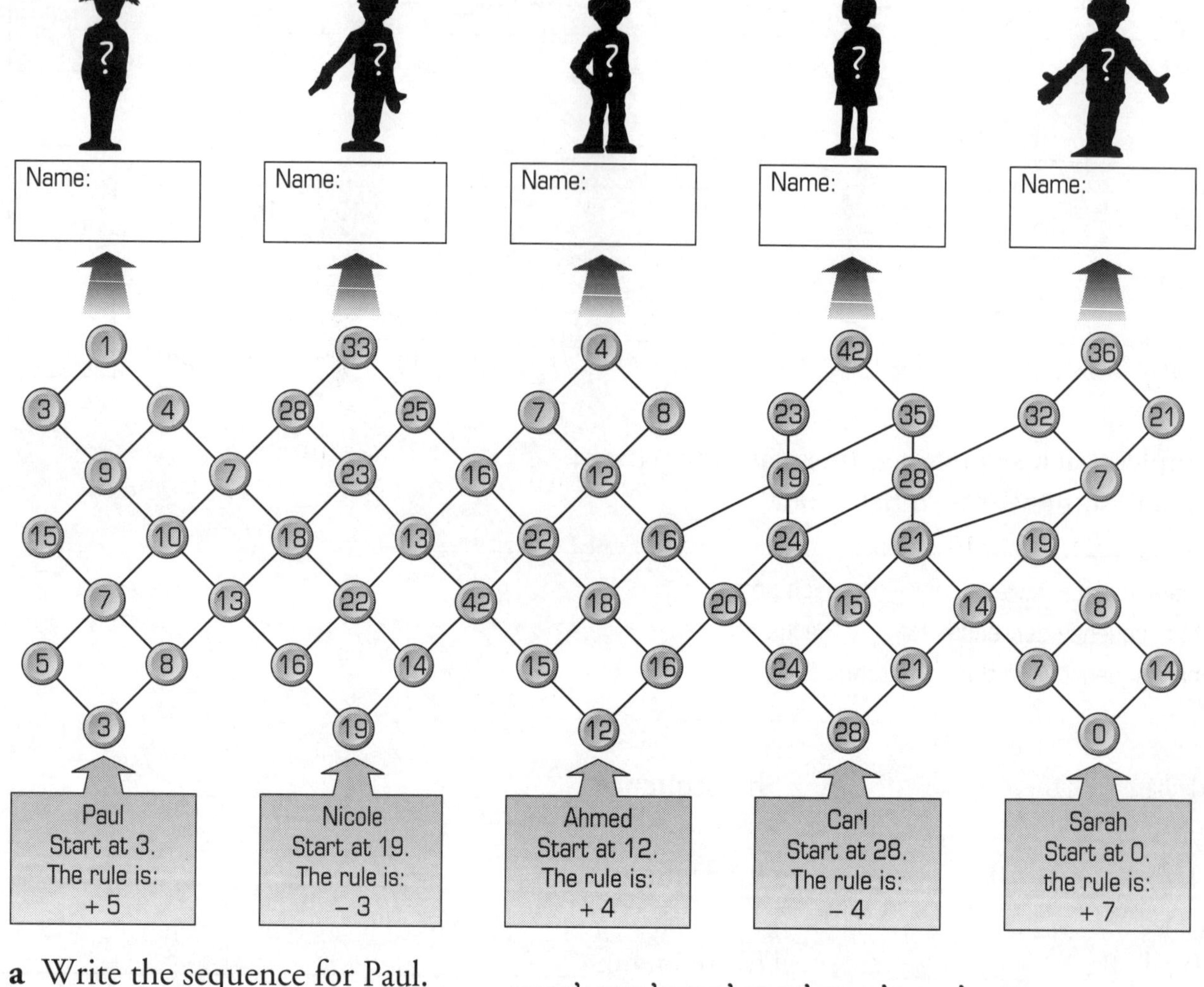

a Write the sequence for Paul. ___ , ___ , ___ , ___ , ___ , ___ , ___

b Write the sequence for Nicole. ___ , ___ , ___ , ___ , ___ , ___ , ___

c Write the sequence for Ahmed. ___ , ___ , ___ , ___ , ___ , ___ , ___

d Write the sequence for Carl. ___ , ___ , ___ , ___ , ___ , ___ , ___

e Write the sequence for Sarah. ___ , ___ , ___ , ___ , ___ , ___ , ___

2 Write the start number and rule for each sequence.

a 5 , 7 , 9 , 11 , 13 , 15 , ... Start at _____ The rule is ________________.

b 2 , 7 , 12 , 17 , 22 , 27 , ... Start at _____ The rule is ________________.

c 20 , 18 , 16 , 14 , 12 , 10 , ... Start at _____ The rule is ________________.

d 20 , 30 , 40 , 50 , 60 , 70, ... Start at _____ The rule is ________________.

A1.4WS Sequences in diagrams

1 The dots on this domino add up to 9 – an odd number.

Draw dots onto these dominoes to make an ...

a

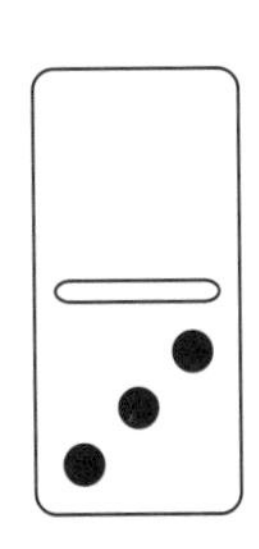

... even number

b

... odd number

c

... even number

d

... odd number

e

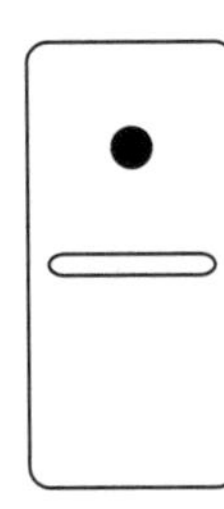

... even number

2 In this zigzag you can only move to a joining square.

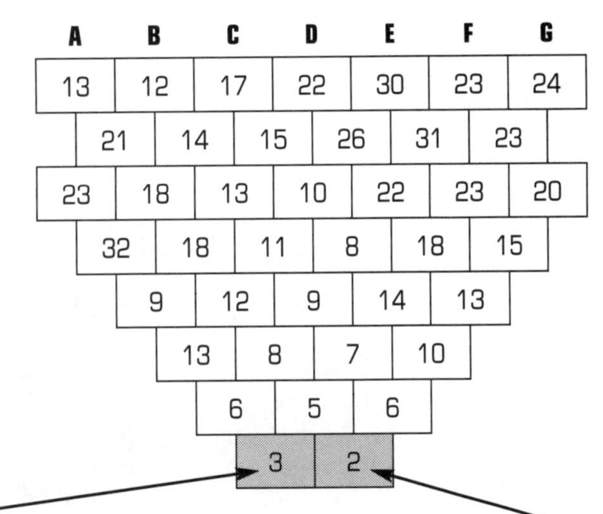

a Start at 3.
Follow only increasing odd numbers.

Write the sequence of odd numbers:

3, ___, ___, ___, ___, ___, ___, ___

Which letter do you arrive at? _______

Write the rule.

The rule is: __________________________

____

b Start at 2.
Follow only increasing even numbers.

Write the sequence of even numbers:

2, ___, ___, ___, ___, ___, ___, ___

Which letter do you arrive at? _______

Write the rule.

The rule is: __________________________

____

A1.5WS Doing and undoing

1 Fill in the second operation that undoes the first one.

a
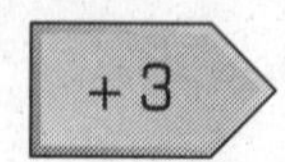

b
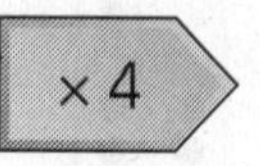

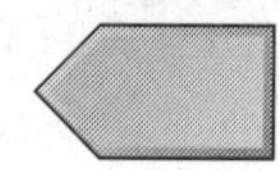

c

d
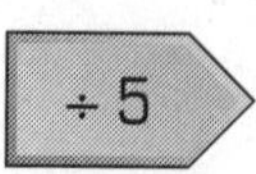

2

F moves a robot forwards.
F3 means go forwards 3 squares.
R means turn right.
L means turn left.
T means turn around.

To move the robot from A to B you write:
F3 – R – F2

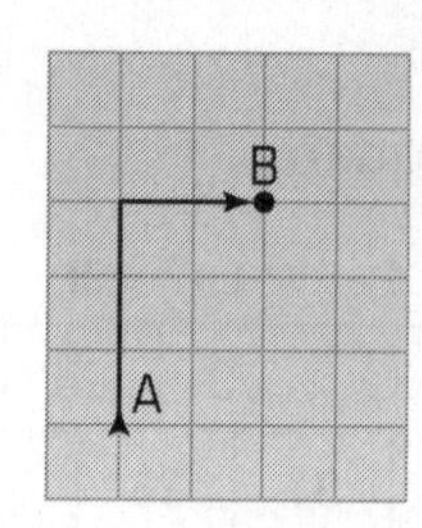

To take the robot back you reverse all the instructions:
T – F2 – L – F3

Draw the path of the robot for:

a F2 – R – F1 – R – F3

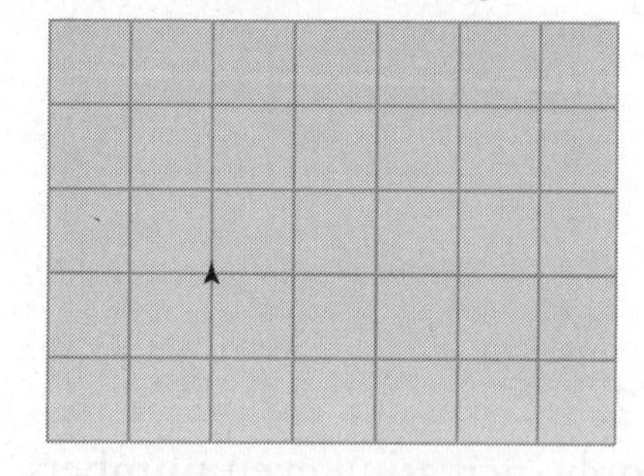

b F1 – L – F3 – R – F2

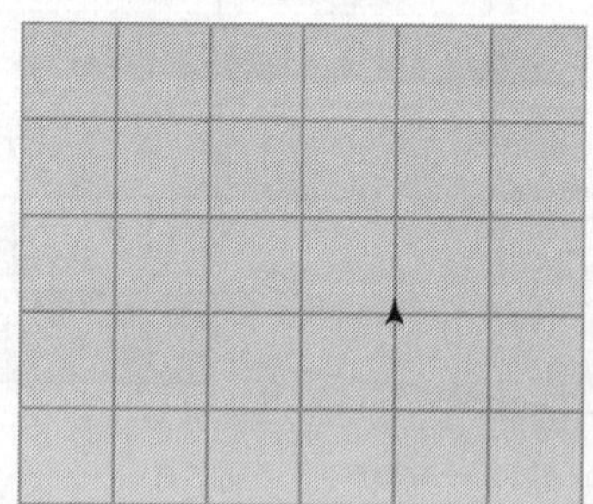

3 For each diagram:

- Give instructions to move the robot from A to B.
- Give the reverse instructions to move the robot back to B.

a

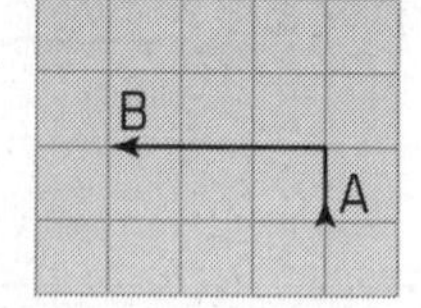

A to B: ______________________

B to A: ______________________

b

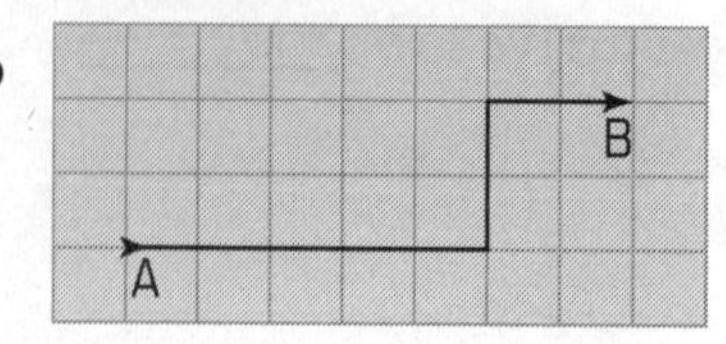

A to B: ______________________

B to A: ______________________

A1.6WS Operation machines

1 Work out these calculations

a $2 + 5 =$ ____	**b** $9 - 3 =$ ____	**c** $10 \times 2 =$ ____	**d** $15 \div 3 =$ ____
e $12 - 4 =$ ____	**f** $16 \div 4 =$ ____	**g** $4 \times 10 =$ ____	**h** $6 + 12 =$ ____
i $20 \div 5 =$ ____	**j** $30 + 50 =$ ____	**k** $5 + 27 =$ ____	**l** $38 - 4 =$ ____
m $22 - 15 =$ ____	**n** $6 \times 7 =$ ____	**o** $24 \div 4 =$ ____	**p** $20 \div 10 =$ ____

2 In this machine:

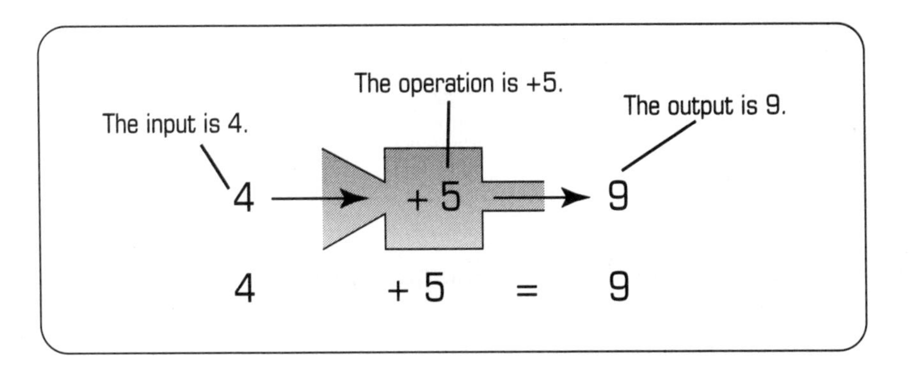

Complete these machines with the correct output.

a

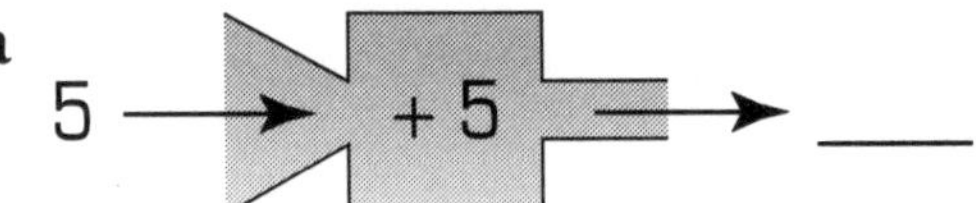

____

b

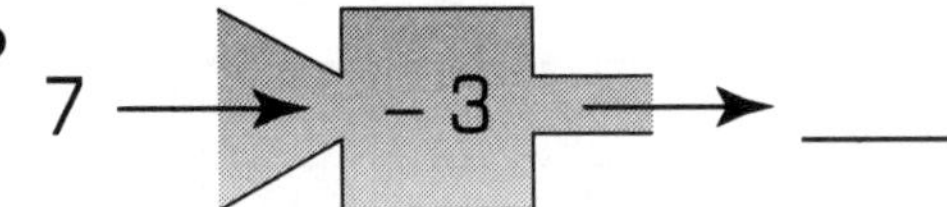

____

c

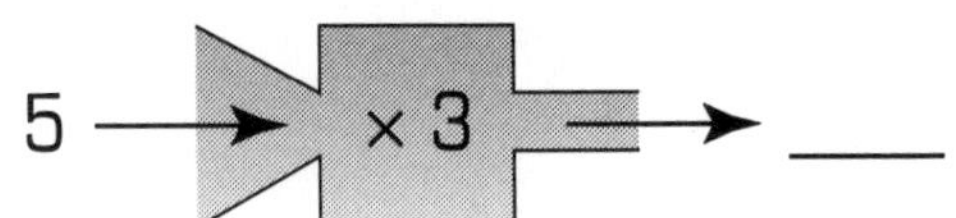

____

d

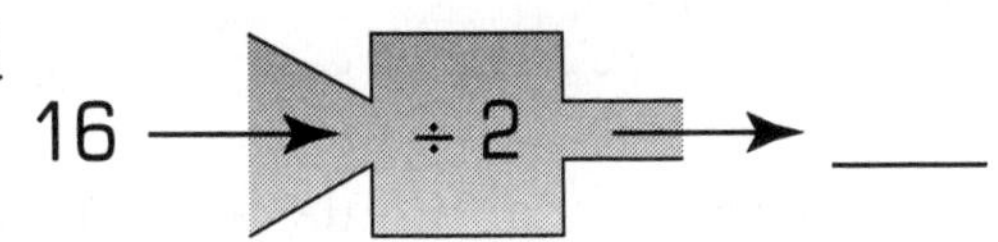

____

e

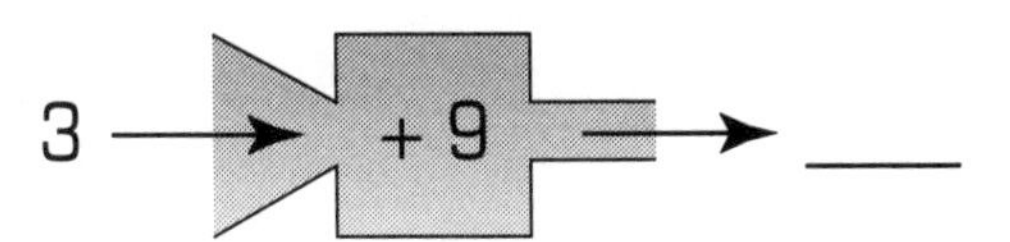

____

f 12 → − 5 → ____

g

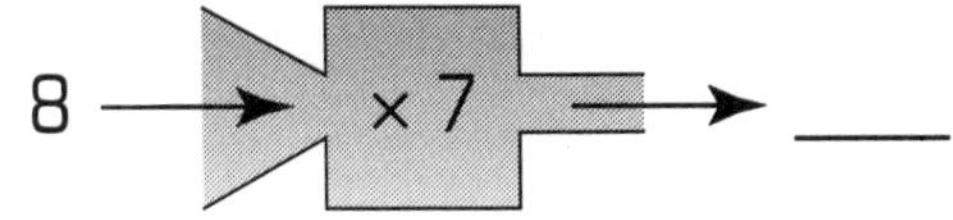

____

h 49 → ÷ 7 → ____

N1.1WS Place value

1 Here are three digits: 

a What is the smallest number you can make?

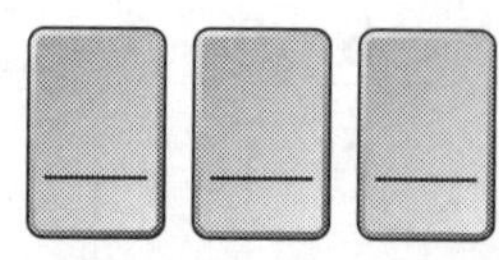

b What is the largest number you can make?

2 What numbers are shown here?

a 

b 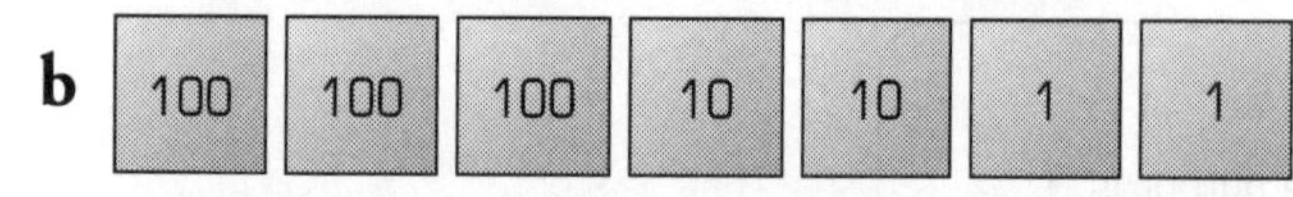

c 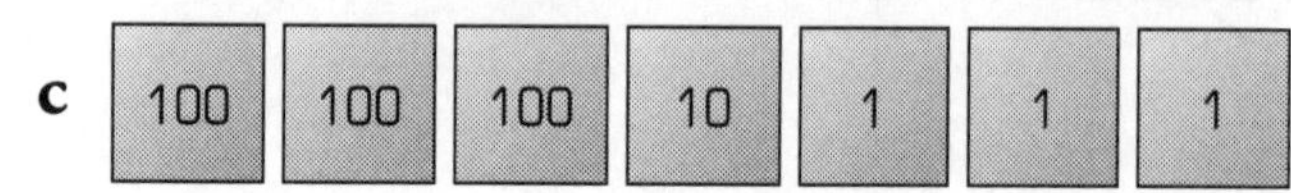

3 Write these numbers as 100s, 10s and units on the cards like question 2.

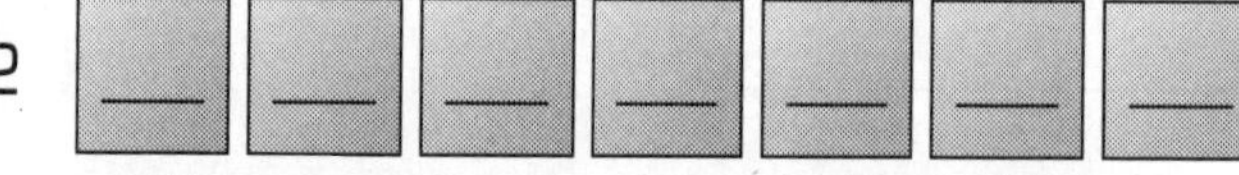

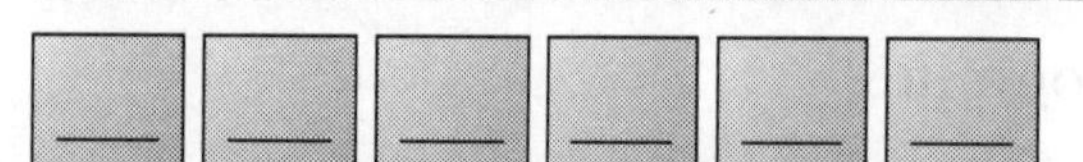

c 420 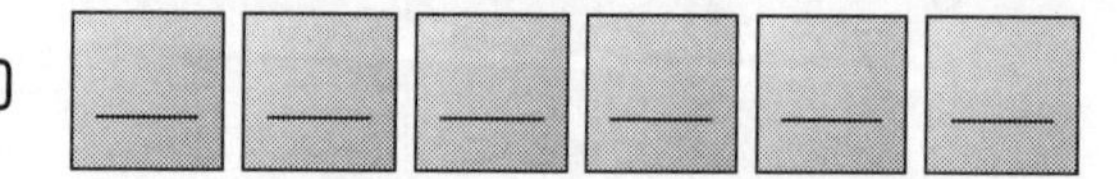

d 205 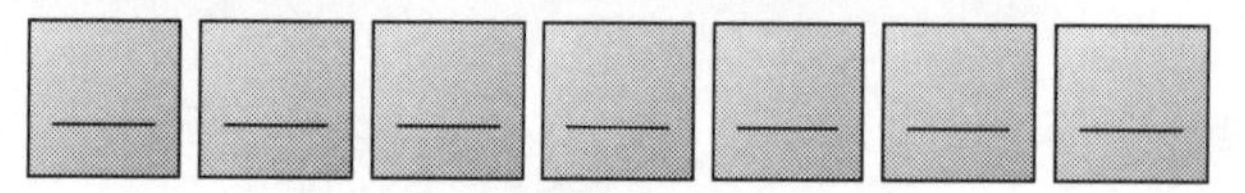

4 Point to these decimal numbers using arrows.

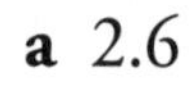

c 5.2

d 0.7

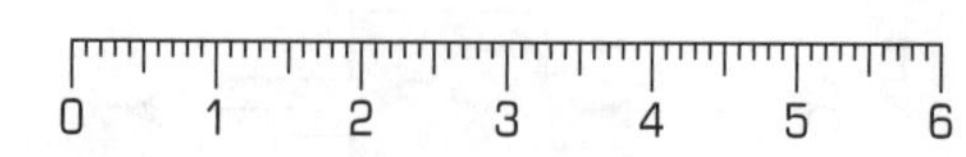

Negative numbers

1 On this number line the arrow points to position 9.

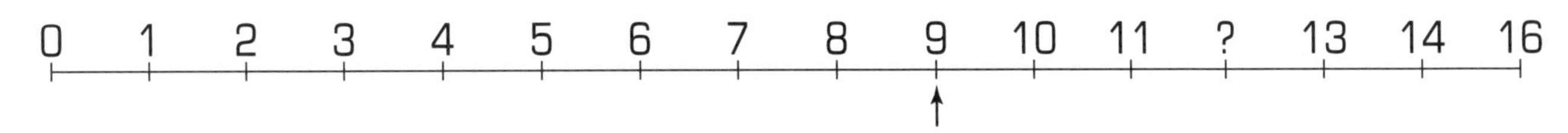

a Draw arrows to point to these positions.
Label the arrows with their letters.

A 5 **B** 3 **C** 11 **D** 8 **E** 0

b Find the ? mark on the line. Write the correct number above it.

c Which number is in the wrong place? Answer: ___________

2 Thermometers measure temperature.

Write the missing temperatures on these thermometers.

a

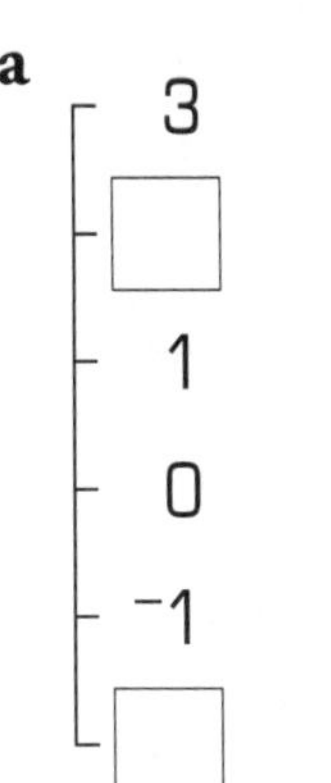

b

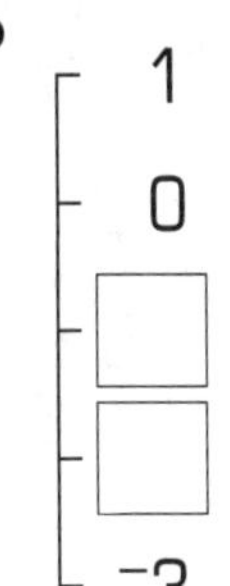

c

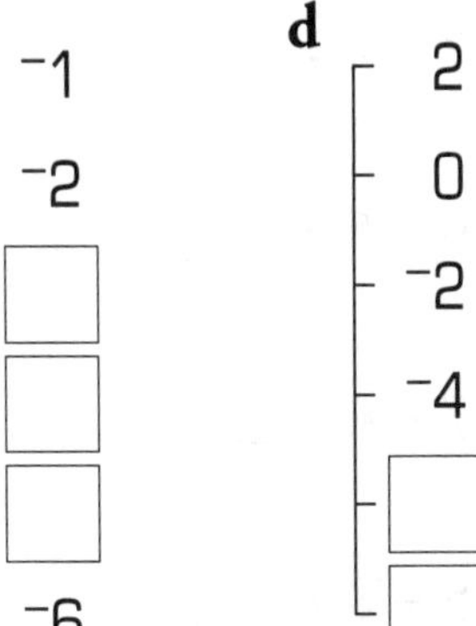

d

2
0
⁻2
⁻4

3 Put the missing numbers into the boxes on this number line.

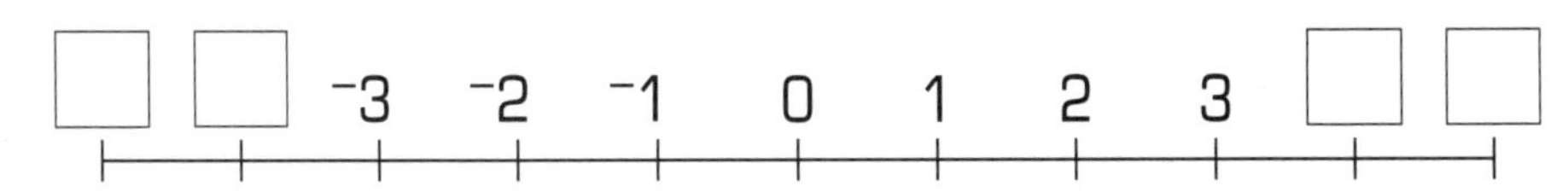

4 Complete this number line that starts at ⁻10.

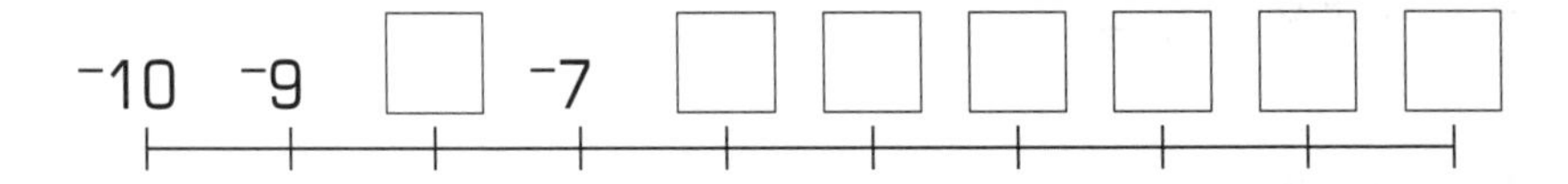

N1.3WS Adding and subtracting with negatives

1 Complete these problems.
Use the number line to help you.

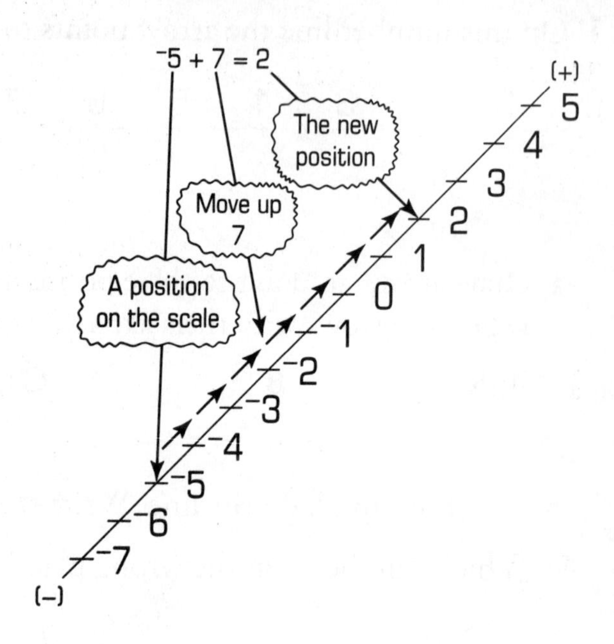

a $^{-}5+7=$ ____ **b** $^{-}3+5=$ ____

c $^{-}4+8=$ ____ **d** $^{-}6+7=$ ____

e $^{-}2+6=$ ____ **f** $^{-}7+5=$ ____

g $^{-}6+6=$ ____ **h** $^{-}2+8=$ ____

i $^{-}9+7=$ ____ **j** $^{-}4+10=$ ____

2 Complete these problems.
Use the number line to help you.

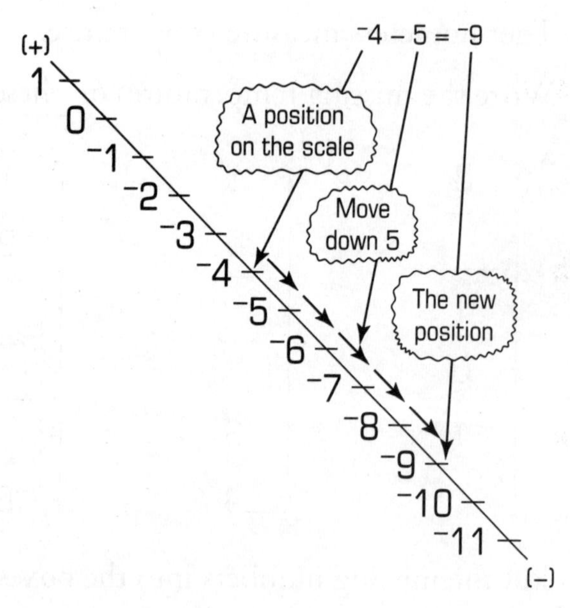

a $^{-}5-3=$ ____ **b** $^{-}3-4=$ ____

c $^{-}1-8=$ ____ **d** $^{-}6-5=$ ____

e $^{-}2-6=$ ____ **f** $^{-}7-4=$ ____

g $^{-}6-6=$ ____ **h** $^{-}5-8=$ ____

i $^{-}9-4=$ ____ **j** $^{-}5-10=$ ____

3 Complete these problems.

a $^{-}4+9=$ ____ **b** $^{-}3-7=$ ____

c $^{-}5-12=$ ____ **d** $^{-}9+6=$ ____

e $^{-}9+9=$ ____ **f** $^{-}5-5=$ ____

g $^{-}12+5=$ ____ **h** $^{-}8-9=$ ____

N1.4WS Mental addition

Use these number lines to help you add these numbers.
The first one is done for you.

1 13 + 14 = 27

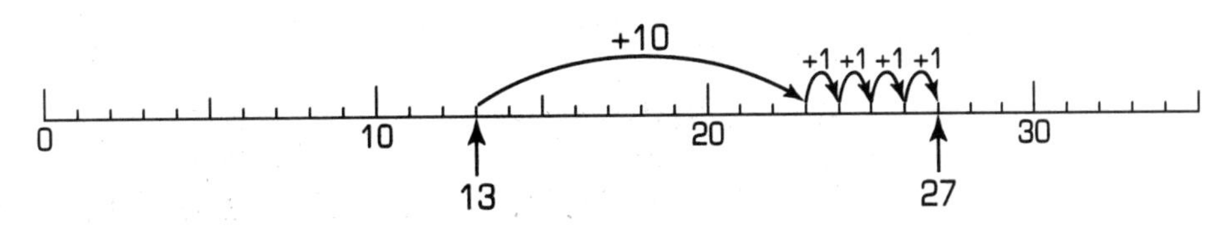

2 20 + 8 = _____

20 30 40 50

3 50 + 18 = _____

50 60 70 80

4 40 + 29 = _____

40 50 60 70

5 23 + 20 = _____

10 20 30 40

6 10 + 19 = _____

10 20 30

7 40 + 32 = _____

40 50 60 70 80

8 26 + 33 = _____

20 30 40 50 60

9 11 + 29 = _____

0 10 20 30 40

N1.6WS Multiplying by 10

When you multiply a number by 10 you move the digits one place to the left:

$3 \times 10 = 30$ $16 \times 10 = 160$

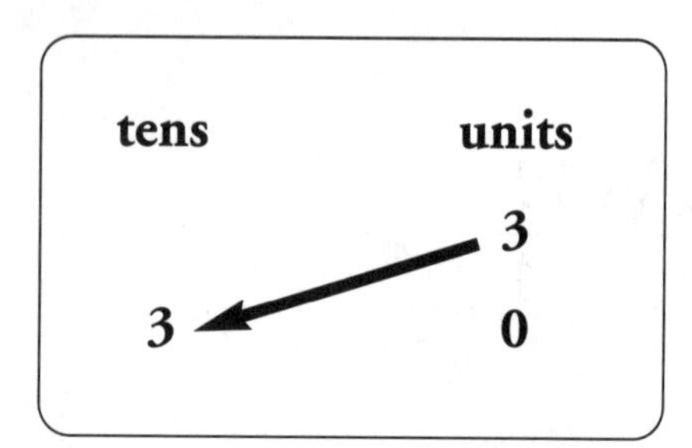

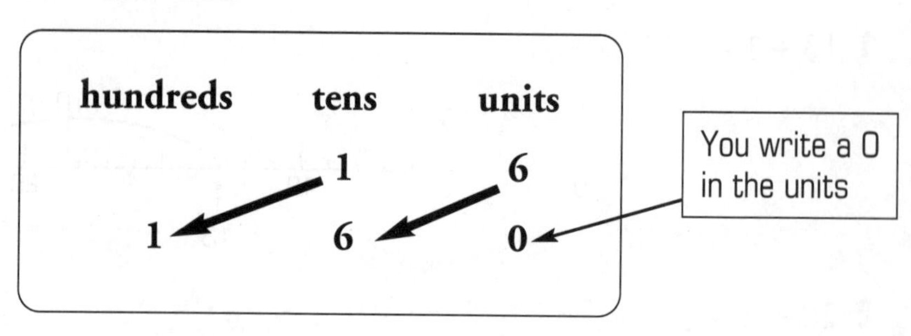

1 Multiply these numbers by 10. Put the digits in the correct place.
Remember to put a 0 in the empty units place.

		hundreds	tens	units
a	$6 \times 10 =$			
b	$9 \times 10 =$			
c	$5 \times 10 =$			
d	$8 \times 10 =$			
e	$10 \times 10 =$			

		hundreds	tens	units
f	$12 \times 10 =$			
g	$23 \times 10 =$			
h	$40 \times 10 =$			
i	$51 \times 10 =$			
j	$83 \times 10 =$			

2 Complete this spider diagram.
Multiply the numbers in the circles by 10 and write the answers in the squares.

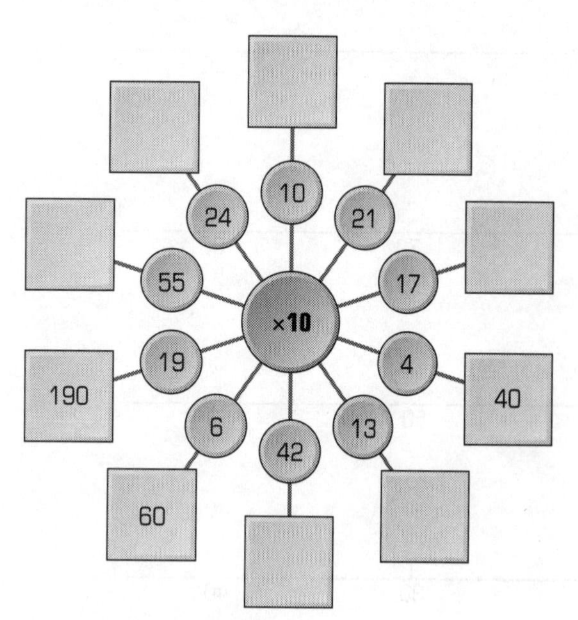

S1.1WS Measurements and scales

1 Write these units of measurement in the correct list.

month	kilogram	second	centimetre	
year	minute	tonne	week	kilometre
hour	gram	millimetre	day	metre

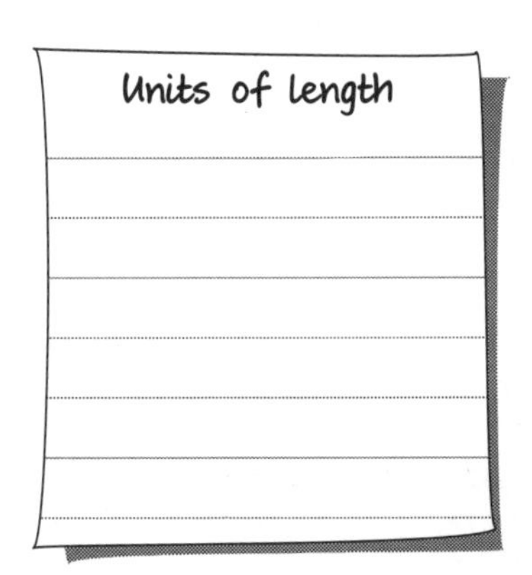

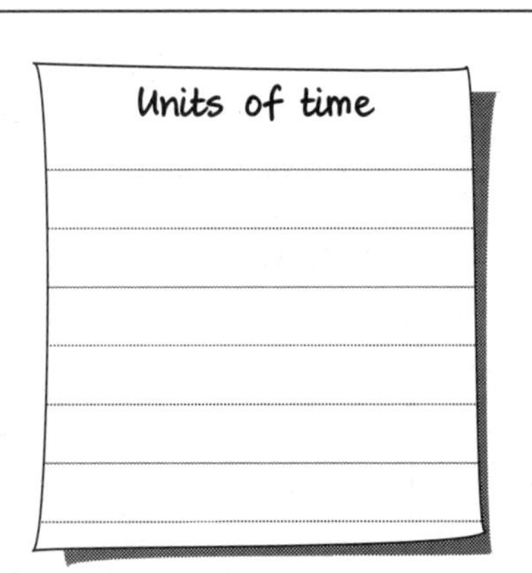

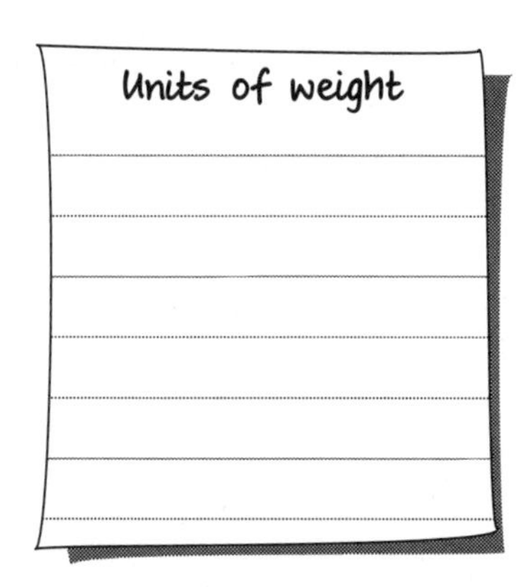

2 What readings are shown on these scales?

a 20 30 = ______ kg

b 30 40 50 = ______ km/h

c 200 300 = ______ ml

d 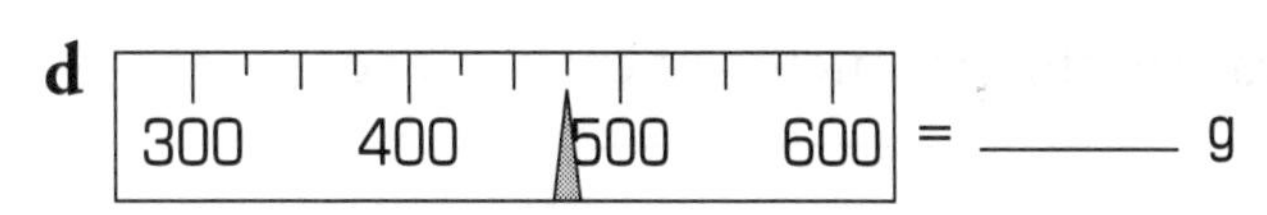

= ______ g

3 Measure these lines using a ruler.

a ______ cm

b ______ cm

c ______ cm

d ______ cm

e ______ cm

4 Measure the length and width of this rectangle and write on your answers.

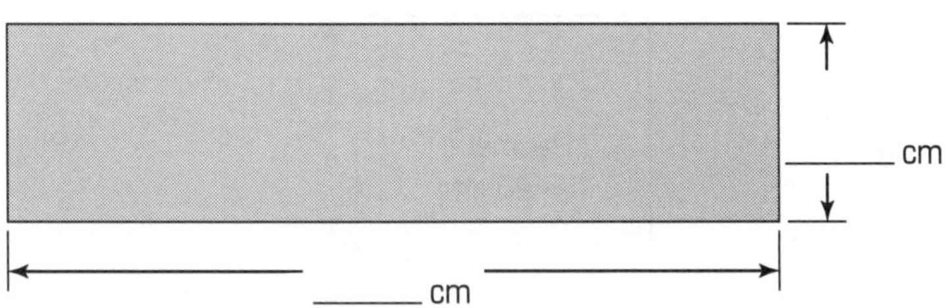

______ cm

______ cm

S1.2WS Perimeter

1 What is the perimeter of each shape?

a

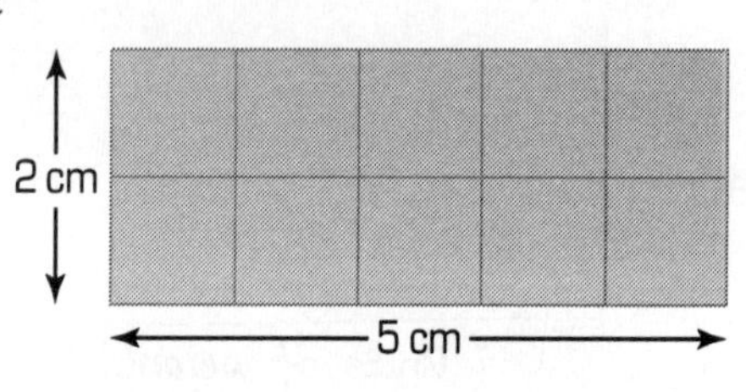

Perimeter = _______ cm

b

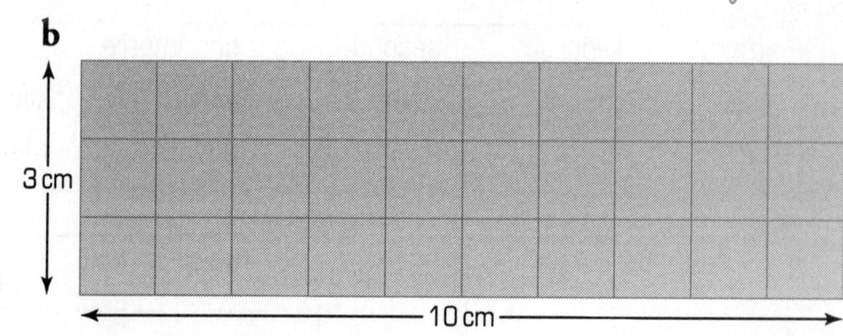

Perimeter = _______ cm

c

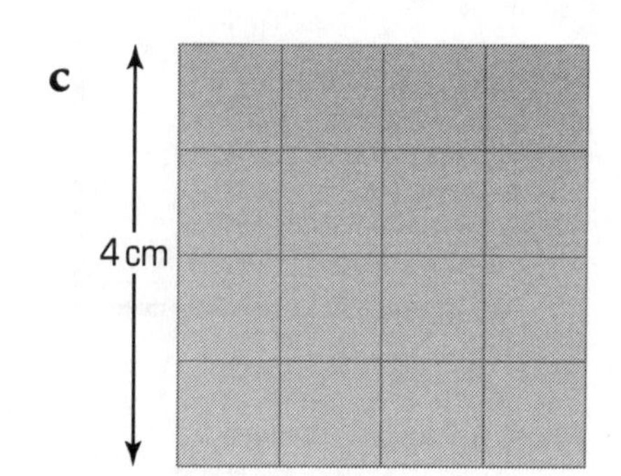

Perimeter = _______ cm

d

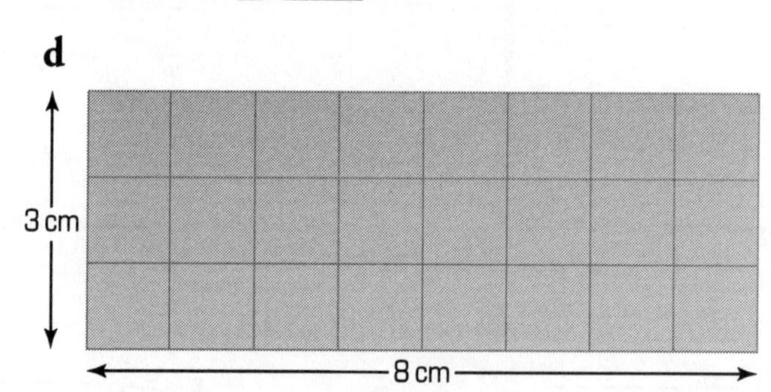

Perimeter = _______ cm

2 Measure the perimeter of each shape.

a

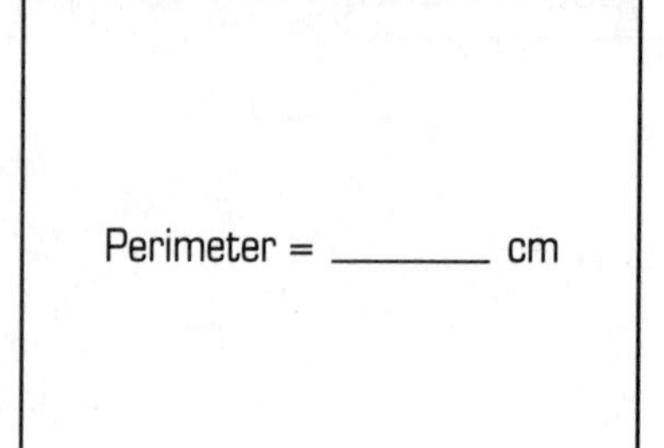

b

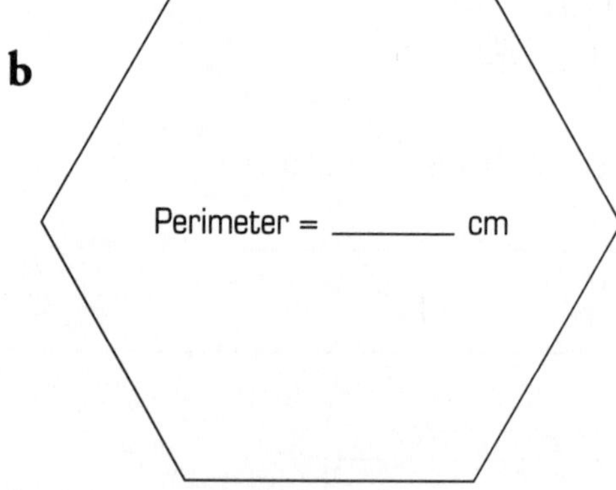

c

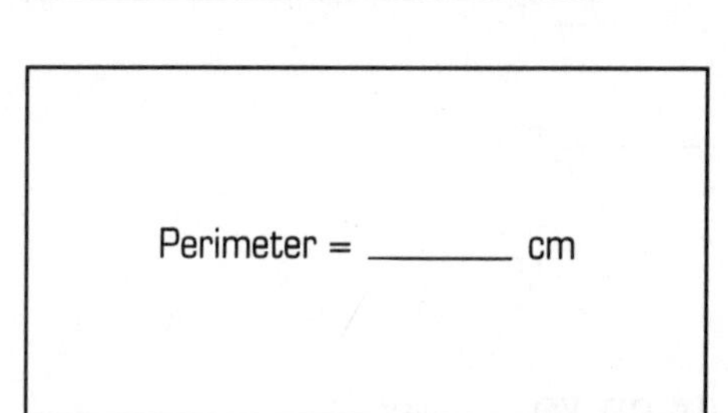

d

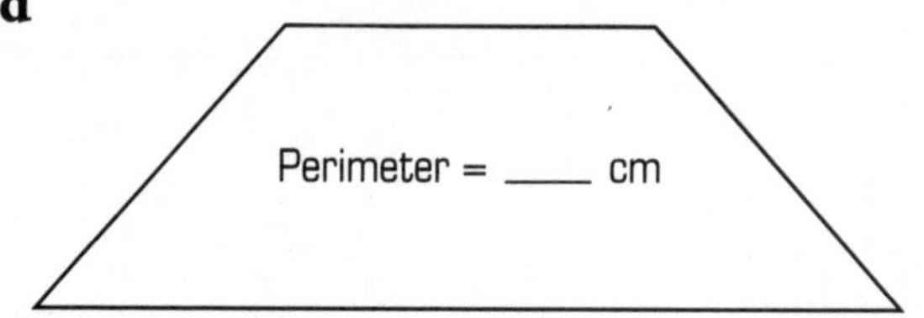

3 Challenge

This is a square.

The perimeter is 20 cm.

What is the length of each side? _________ cm

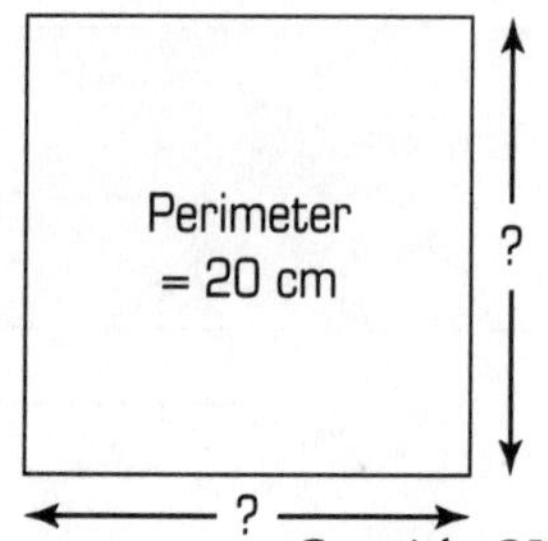

This is a plan of the ground floor of a palace.
The measurements of each room are in metres.

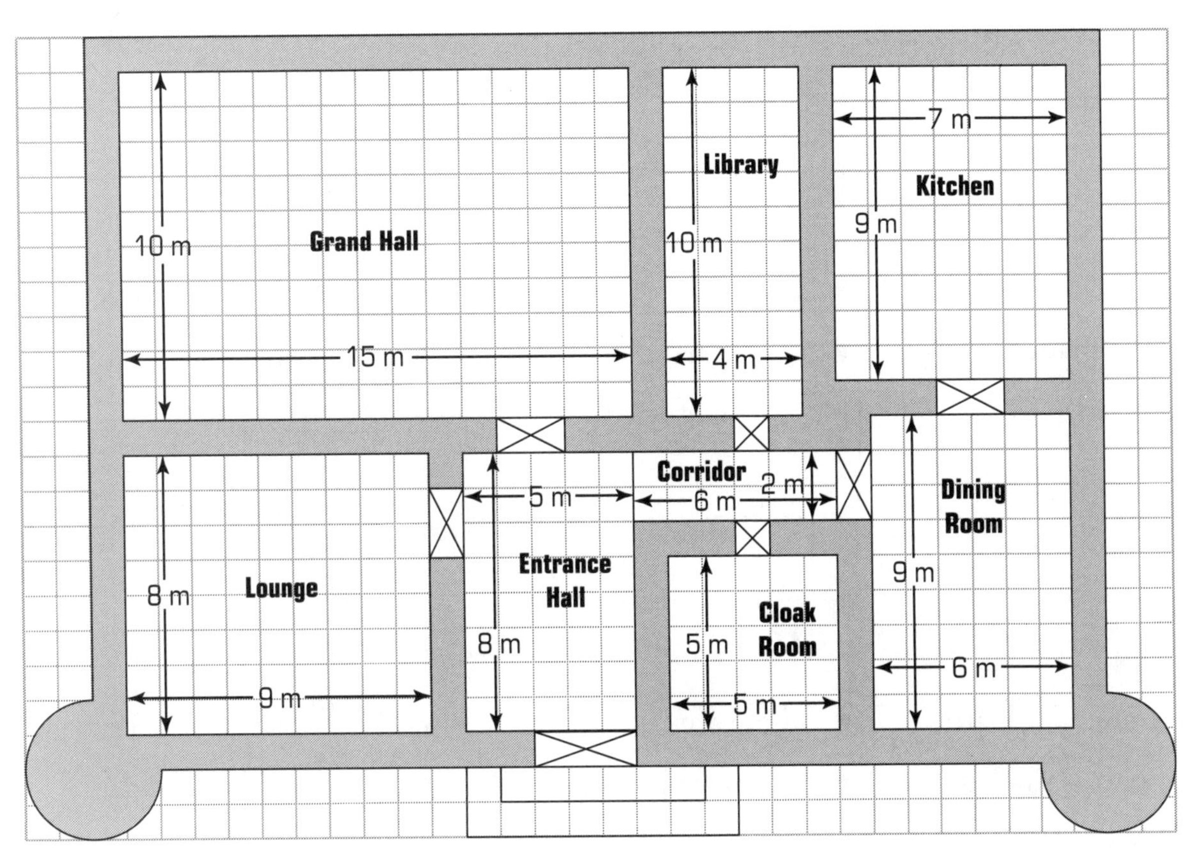

1 What is the perimeter of:

a The Cloak Room ________ m **b** The Grand Hall ________ m

c The Lounge ________ **d** The Kitchen ________

e The Dining Room ________ **f** The Library ________

▶ Area of a rectangle = length × width.

Your answers should be in square metres (m^2)

2 What is the area of:

a The Cloak Room ________ m^2 **b** The Library ________ m^2

c The Dining Room ________ m^2 **d** The Grand Hall ________ m^2

e The Lounge ________ **f** The Kitchen ________

g The Entrance Hall ________ **h** The Corridor ________

N2.1WS Understanding fractions

1 Complete these sentences by looking at each shape.

The first one is done for you.

a

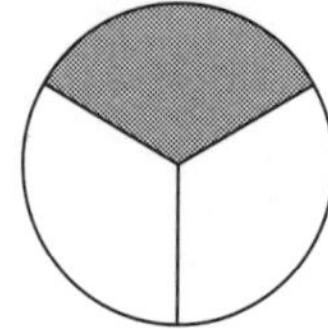

- There are **3** parts.
- **1** part is shaded.
- $\frac{1}{3}$ is shaded.

b

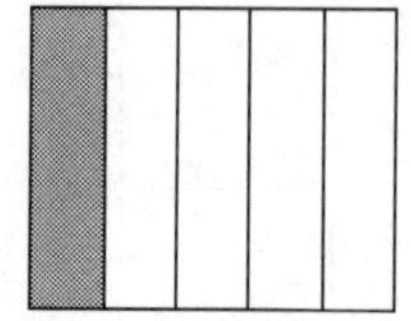

- There are ____ parts.
- ____ part is shaded.
- ____ is shaded.

c

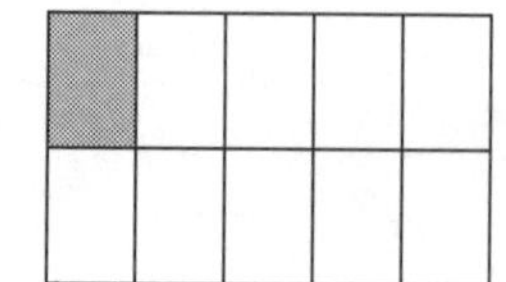

- There are ____ parts.
- ____ part is shaded.
- ____ is shaded.

d

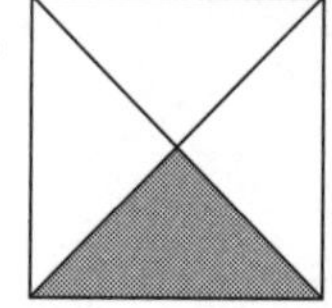

- There are ____ parts.
- ____ part is shaded.
- ____ is shaded.

e

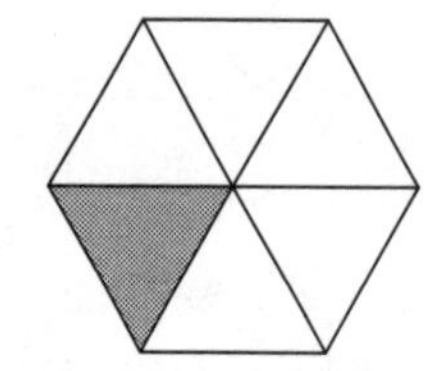

- There are ____ parts.
- ____ part is shaded.
- ____ is shaded.

f

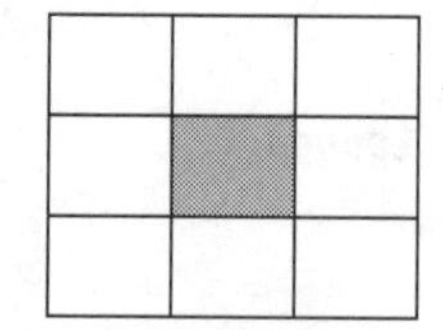

- There are ____ parts.
- ____ part is shaded.
- ____ is shaded.

2

This shape is divided into 3 parts.
2 parts are shaded.
$\frac{2}{3}$ of the whole shape is shaded.

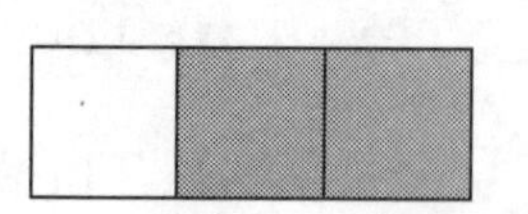

What fraction of each shape is shaded?

a

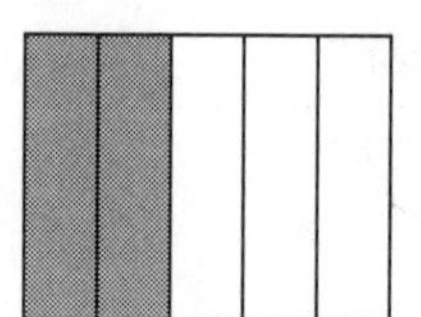

____

b

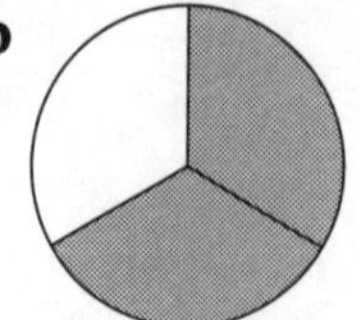

____

c

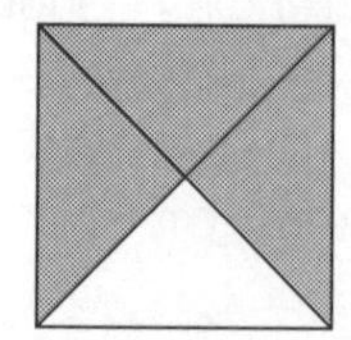

____

d

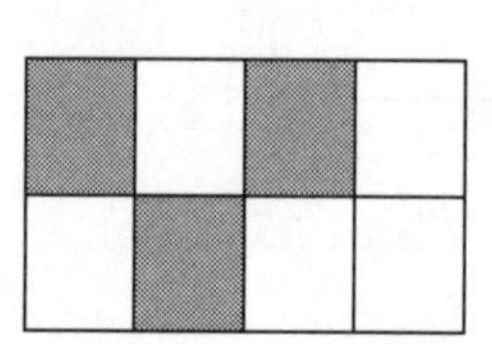

____

e

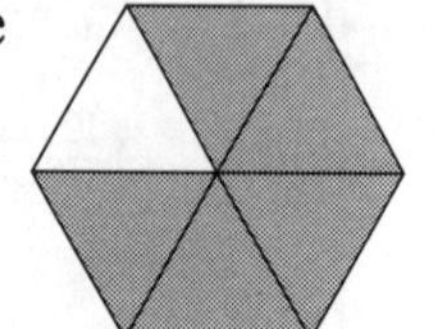

____

f

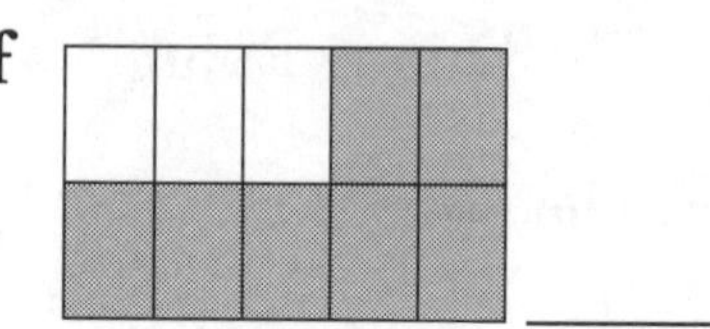

____

Comparing fractions

1 **a** Divide this rectangle into quarters ($\frac{1}{4}$s).

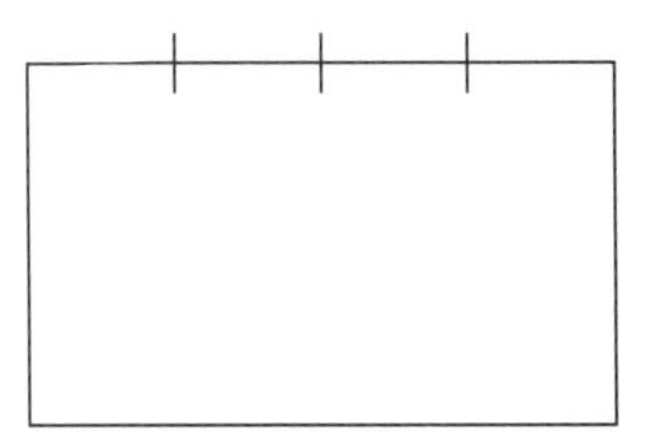

Colour in $\frac{1}{4}$

b Divide this rectangle into halves ($\frac{1}{2}$s).

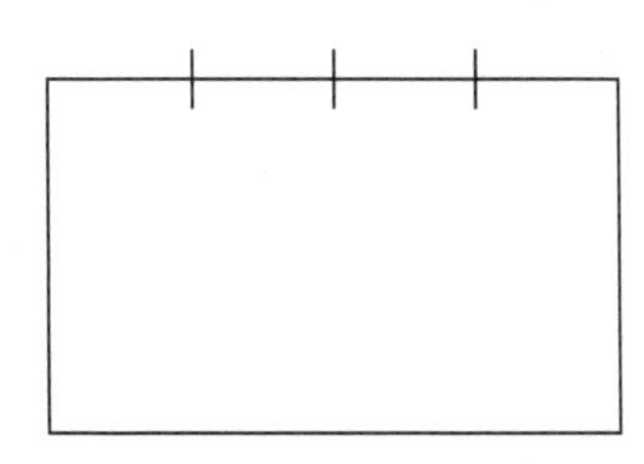

Colour in $\frac{1}{2}$.

c Compare the $\frac{1}{4}$ and the $\frac{1}{2}$.

Which is the larger area? ___________

2 **a** Colour $\frac{1}{2}$ of this hexagon.

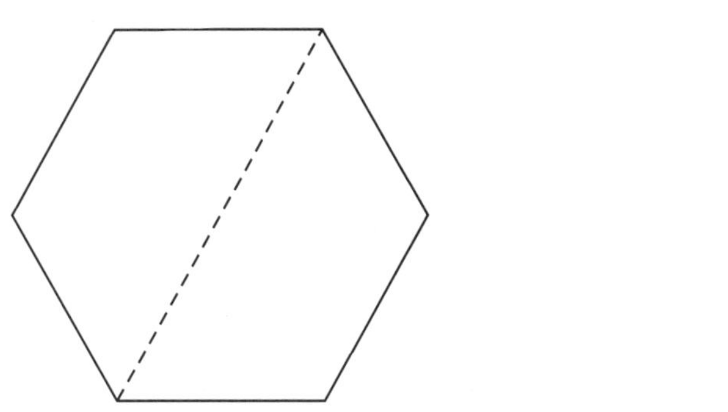

b Colour $\frac{1}{6}$ of this hexagon.

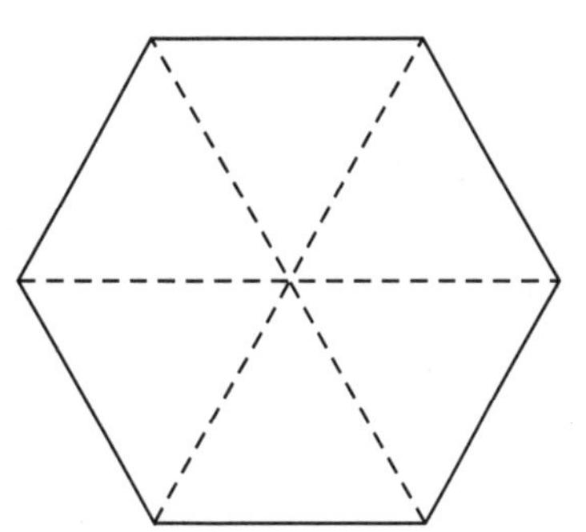

The hexagons are exactly the same.

c Write in a greater than (>) or less than (<) sign to compare the fractions.

$\frac{1}{6}$ ☐ $\frac{1}{2}$

d Colour $\frac{5}{6}$ of the second hexagon.
Write in a > or < sign to compare the fractions.

$\frac{5}{6}$ ☐ $\frac{1}{2}$

3 Steve and Claire have to share these marbles fairly.
Claire wants $\frac{6}{12}$ of the marbles.
Show on the drawing that this is a fair share.

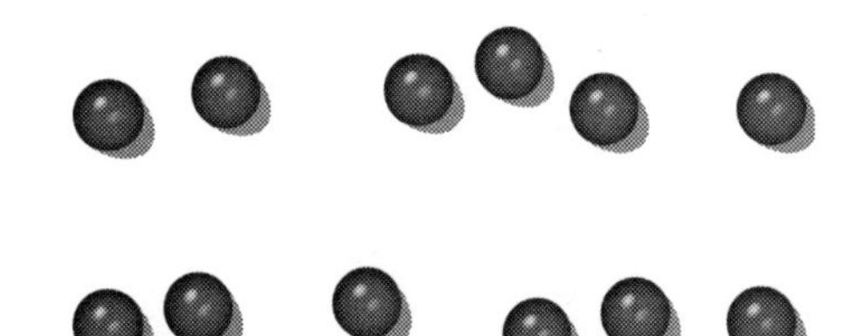

N2.3WS Fractions of amounts

1 Here are 10 cubes. Put them in two equal groups.

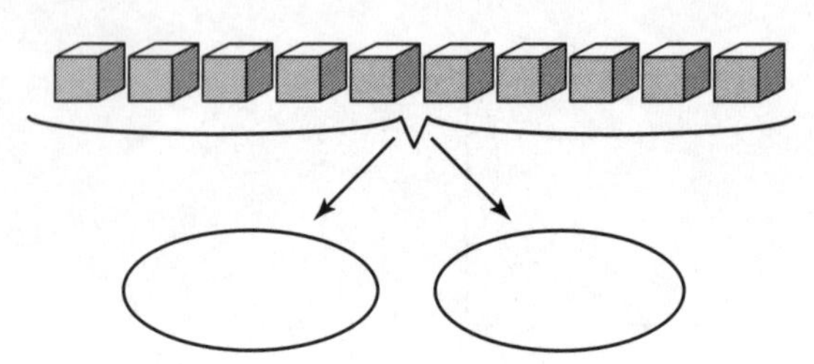

What is $\frac{1}{2}$ of 10?

Answer: ______

2 Here are 15 counters. Put them in three equal groups.

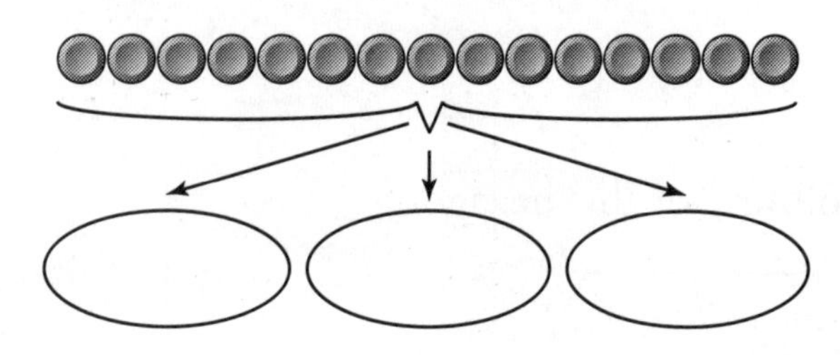

What is $\frac{1}{3}$ of 15?

Answer: ______

3 Use the multiplication grid to help you find:

a $\frac{1}{2}$ of 8 = ___ **b** $\frac{1}{3}$ of 9 = ___

c $\frac{1}{4}$ of 16 = ___ **d** $\frac{1}{5}$ of 15 = ___

e $\frac{1}{3}$ of 18 = ___ **f** $\frac{1}{4}$ of 24 = ___

g $\frac{1}{6}$ of 24 = ___ **h** $\frac{1}{2}$ of 12 = ___

i $\frac{1}{5}$ of 30 = ___ **j** $\frac{1}{6}$ of 30 = ___

×	1	2	3	4	5	6
1	1	2	3	4	5	6
2	2	4	6	8	10	12
3	3	6	9	12	15	18
4	4	8	12	16	20	24
5	5	10	15	20	25	30
6	6	12	18	24	30	36

4 Find:

a $\frac{1}{2}$ of 18 = ________ **b** $\frac{1}{2}$ of 24 = ________ **c** $\frac{1}{2}$ of 40 = ________

5 Find:

a $\frac{1}{4}$ of 28 = ________ **b** $\frac{1}{4}$ of 40 = ________ **c** $\frac{1}{4}$ of 32 = ________

6 Find:

a $\frac{1}{3}$ of 24 = ________ **b** $\frac{1}{3}$ of 30 = ________ **c** $\frac{1}{3}$ of 36 = ________

N2.4WS Decimal scales

1 What decimal part of each circle is shaded?

a 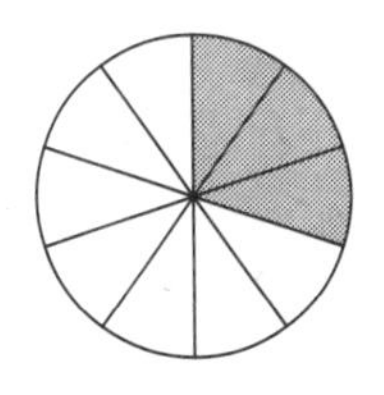

b 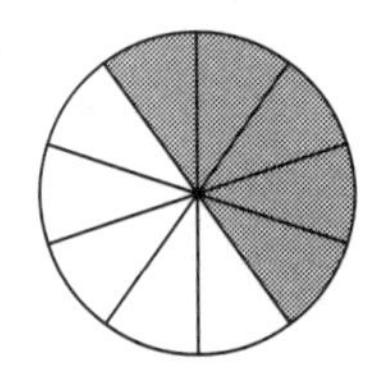

c 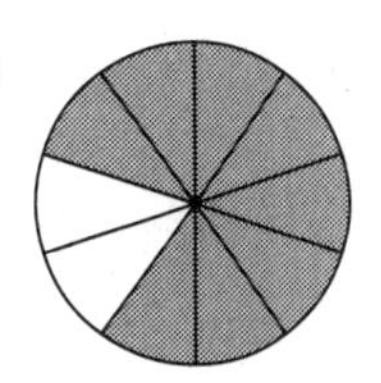

d 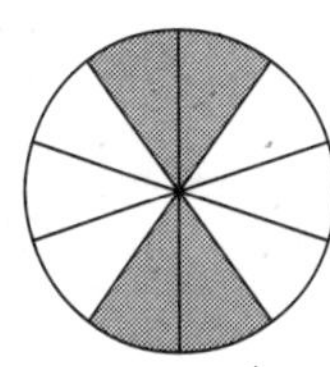

______ is shaded. ______ is shaded. ______ is shaded. ______ is shaded.

2 Each square is one tenth. What decimal numbers are shown here?
The first is done for you.

a 

= 1.4

b 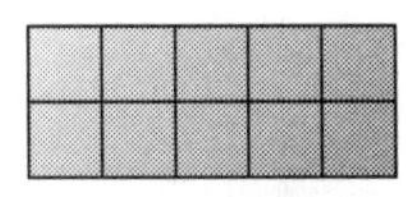

= ________

c 

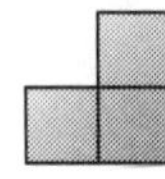

= ________

d 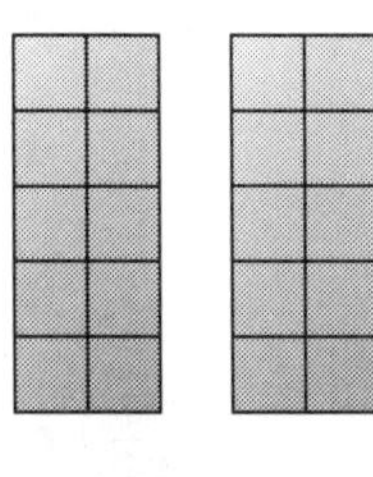

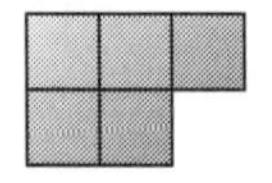

= ________

3 What reading does each scale show?
Write your answer as a decimal.

A = _____

B = _____

C = _____

D = _____

E = _____

F = _____

G = _____

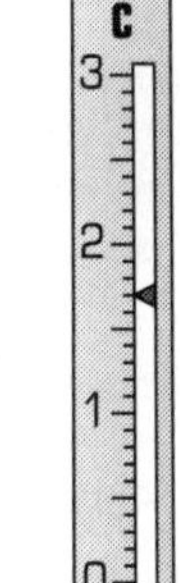

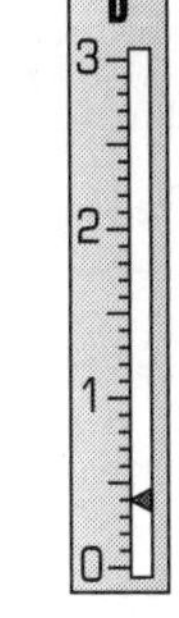

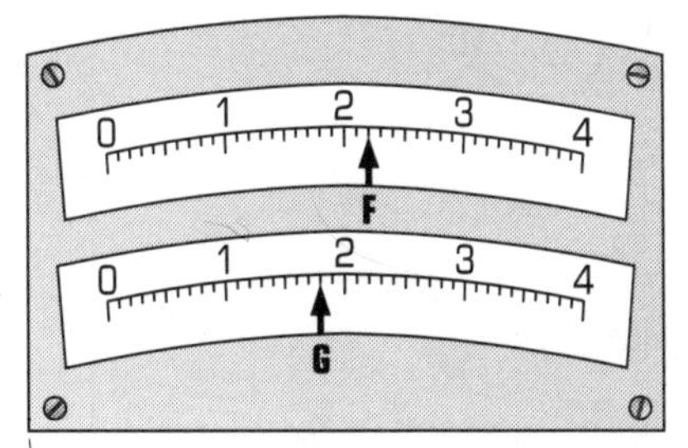

N2.5WS Decimals and percentages

1 Use arrows to join fractions, decimals and percentages of the same value.
The first is done for you.

Fraction	Decimal	Percentage
$\frac{4}{10}$	0.9	10%
$\frac{1}{10}$	0.2	40%
$\frac{3}{10}$	0.6	80%
$\frac{9}{10}$	0.4	30%
$\frac{2}{10}$	0.1	100%
$\frac{7}{10}$	0.8	90%
$\frac{10}{10}$	0.3	60%
$\frac{8}{10}$	0.5	70%
$\frac{6}{10}$	1.0	50%
$\frac{5}{10}$	0.7	20%

2 Use these signs to compare these fractions, decimals and percentages.
The first is done for you.

$>$ means 'is bigger than'
$<$ means 'is smaller than'
$=$ means 'the same as'

a $0.7 > \frac{5}{10}$

b 50% $\square$ 0.8

c $\frac{1}{10}$ $\square$ 10%

d 30% $\square$ $\frac{6}{10}$

e $\frac{8}{10}$ $\square$ 80%

f 0.2 $\square$ $\frac{1}{10}$

g 0.5 $\square$ $\frac{8}{10}$

h 60% $\square$ $\frac{3}{10}$

i 30% $\square$ 0.3

j $\frac{7}{10}$ $\square$ 0.7

k 1.0 $\square$ 80%

l 0.6 $\square$ 70%

m 0.4 $\square$ $\frac{5}{10}$

n 50% $\square$ 0.5

o $\frac{3}{10}$ $\square$ 20%

Finding tenths of amounts

1 Here are 20 beads.

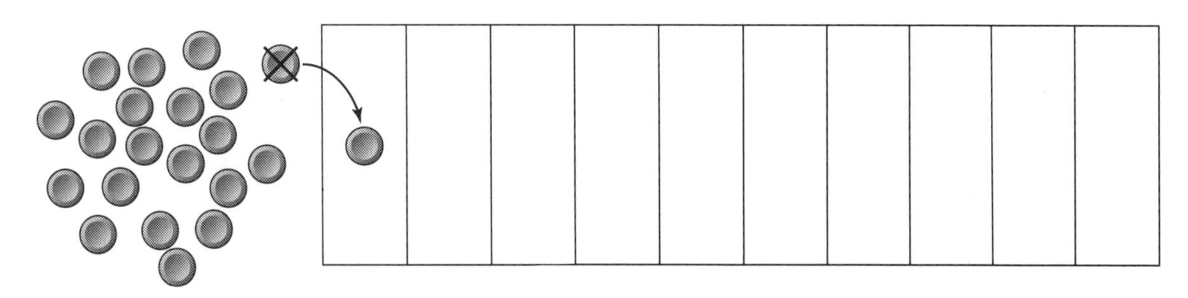

a Share the beads equally between the 10 sections.
Each section is a tenth.

b Use the drawing to link these calculations to their correct answers.
The first one is done for you.

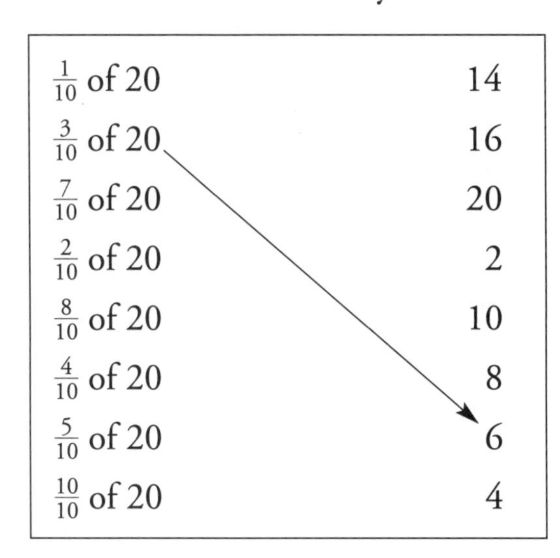

2 This plank measures 10 cm.

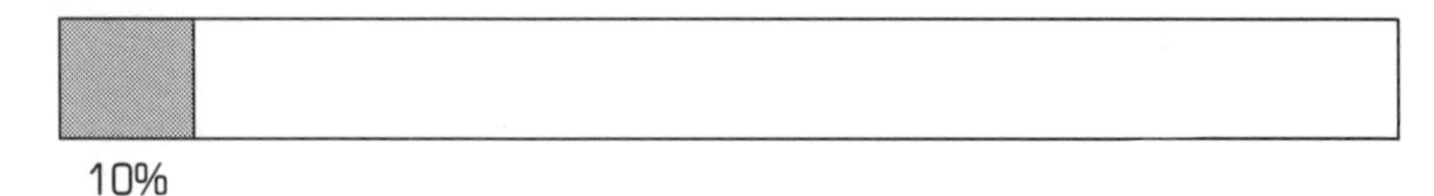

a Divide the plank into exactly 10% sections. The first one has been done for you.

b 10% of the plank has been shaded. Shade another 40%.

c How much of the plank is now shaded? Answer: _______%.

3 **a** Shade 60% of this rectangle.

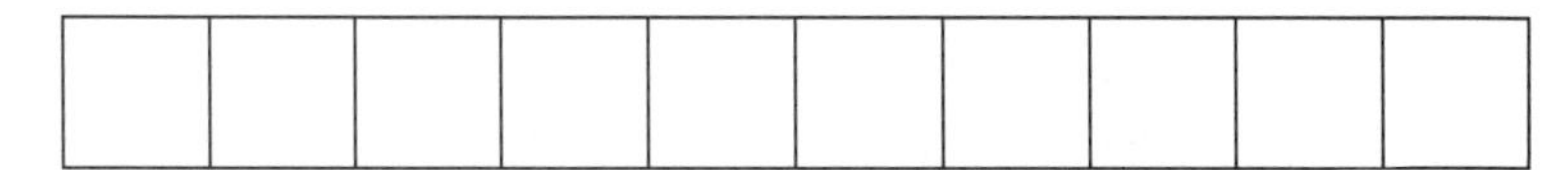

b Use the diagram in question 1 to find 60% of 20. Answer: _______.

D1.1WS The mode

1 How much does each 'tally' show?
The first is done for you.

a 𝍸 || = 7 **b** 𝍸 𝍸 = ___ **c** 𝍸 𝍸 |||| = ___ **d** 𝍸 𝍸 𝍸 𝍸 𝍸 || = ___

2 Show these numbers as a tally.

a 9 = ________________ **b** 12 = ________________

c 15 = ________________ **d** 23 = ________________

3 Class 7M do a survey of hair colour in their class.

Brown	*Red*	*Brown*	*~~Black~~*	*Blond*	*Brown*	*Blond*
~~Black~~	*Blond*	*Brown*	*~~Black~~*	*~~Black~~*	*Brown*	
Blond	*Brown*	*Brown*	*Red*	*Blond*	*~~Black~~*	*Blond*

a Complete this tally of the data.

Colour	Tally	Frequency
Black	𝍸	5
Blond		
Brown		
Red		

b Complete this barchart using the data from the tally chart.

Frequency: 0 1 2 3 4 5 6 7 8

Black Blond Brown Red

Hair colour

c The mode is the biggest group.
What is the modal hair colour?

Answer: ______________.

D1.3WS Levelling

1 Level out each tower of cubes to make equal height towers. This is the mean. Use Multilink cubes. The first has been started for you.

a

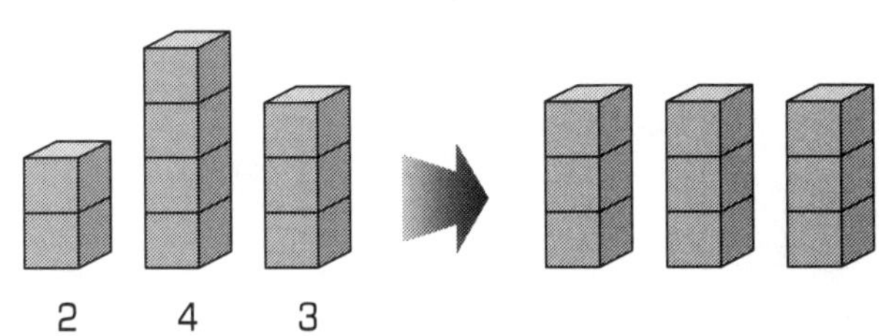

2 4 3

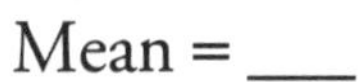

Mean = ___

b

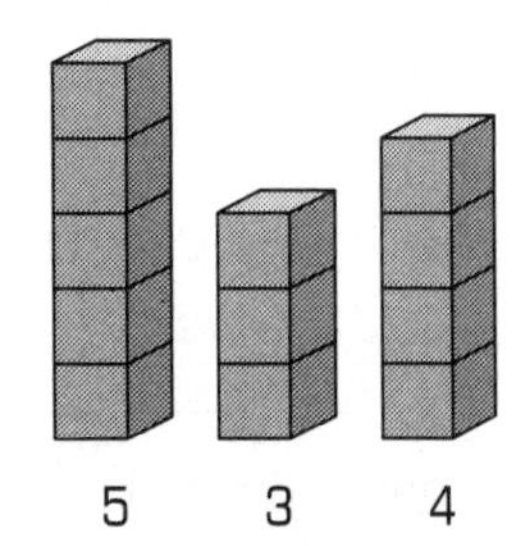

5 3 4

Mean = ___

c

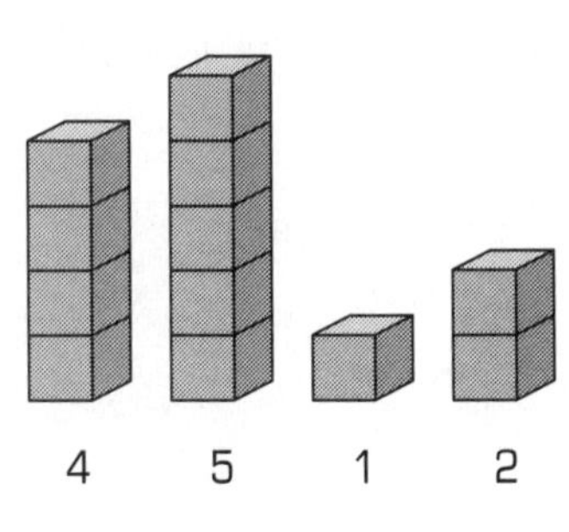

4 5 1 2

Mean = ___

d

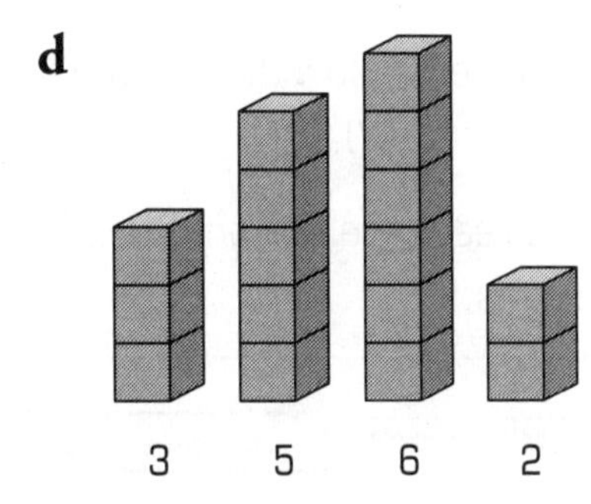

3 5 6 2

Mean = ___

2 How many items would each person have if they were shared out equally?

a

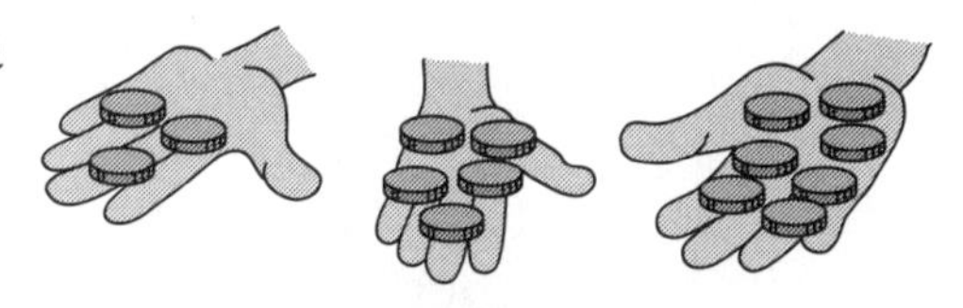

_____ coins

b

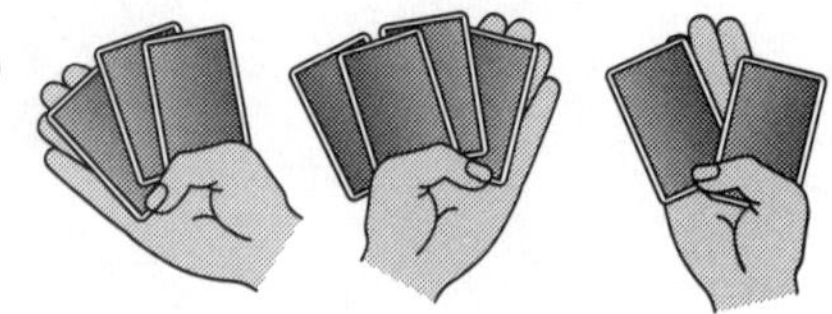

_____ cards

c

_____ pencils

d

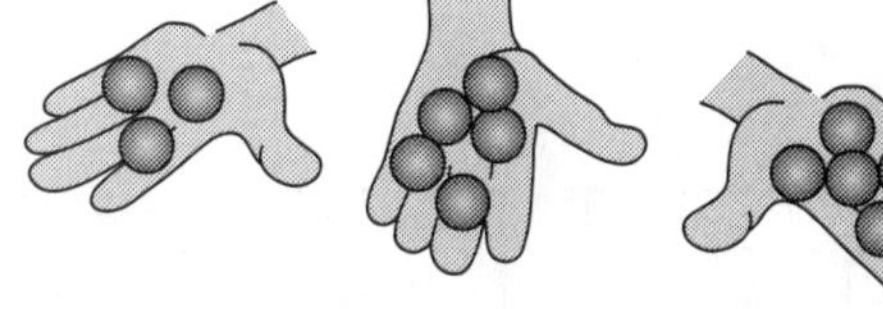

_____ sweets

D1.5WS Describing chance

When you spin two coins, there are three ways they can land.

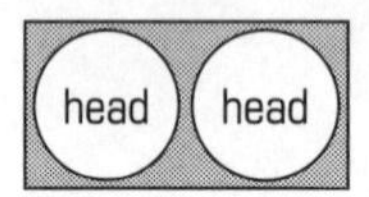

or

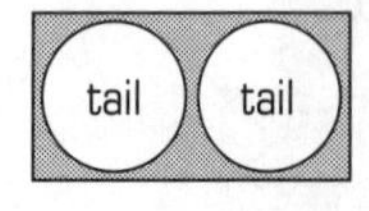

or

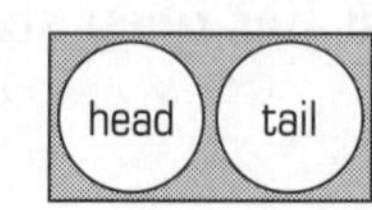

Follow these steps to see if you can guess which way will come up!
You will need two coins.

1. Guess a result – two heads, two tails or a head and a tail.
   You can write: HH, TT or HT.
2. Spin two coins.
3. If the guess is correct follow the tick (✓) to the next level.
   If not, follow the cross (✗).
4. Repeat until you reach the bottom level. This shows your percentage of correct guesses.

You can play the game with other students – take it in turns to guess and use a different colour to mark your results.

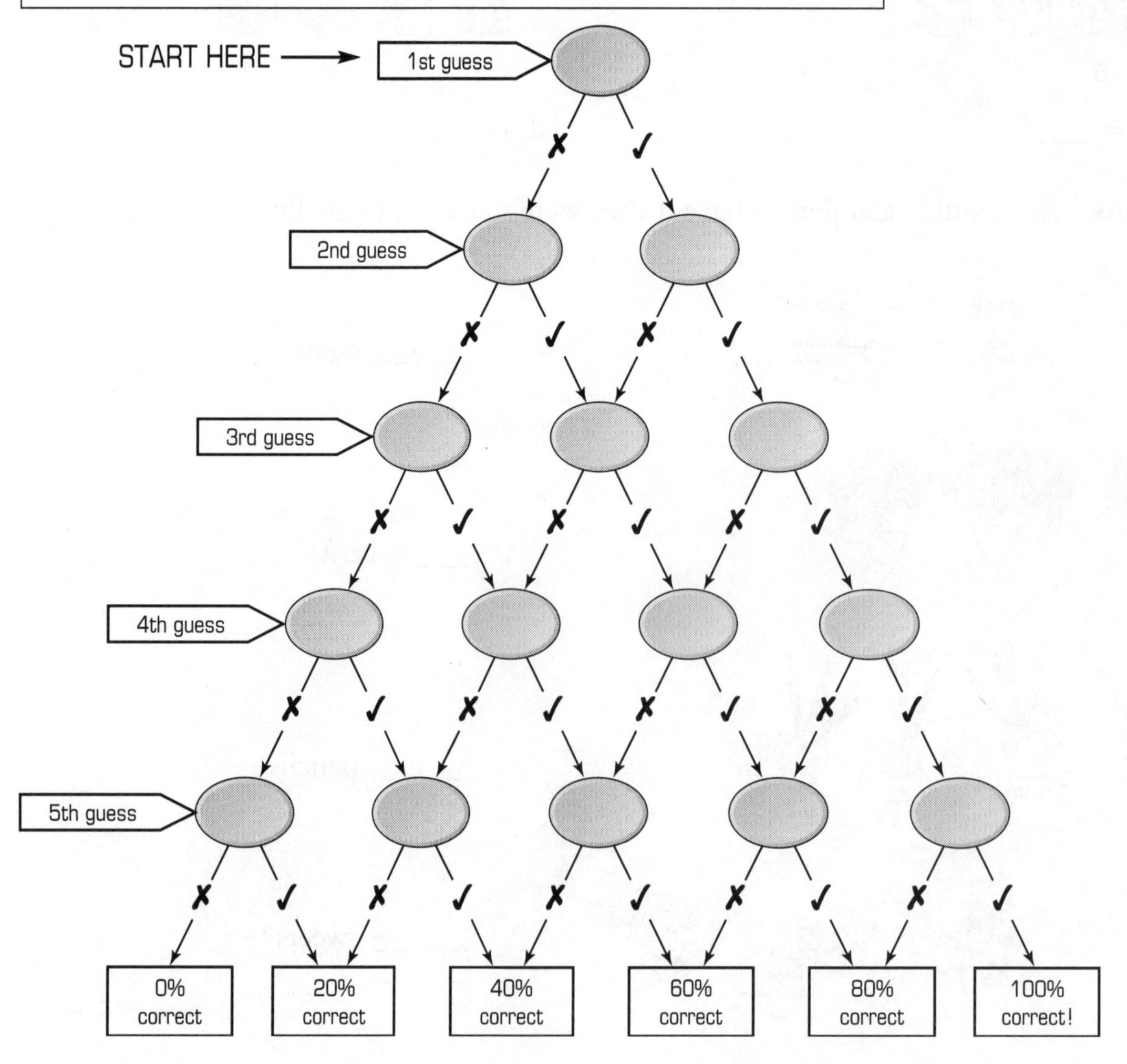

A2.1WS Using letters

1 Josh keeps some of his marbles in a bag.

Can you tell exactly how many marbles are in Josh's bag, without guessing?

Circle the correct answer: Yes or No

2 Josh uses t to stand for the number of marbles in his bag.
He has t marbles in the bag and another 4 marbles.

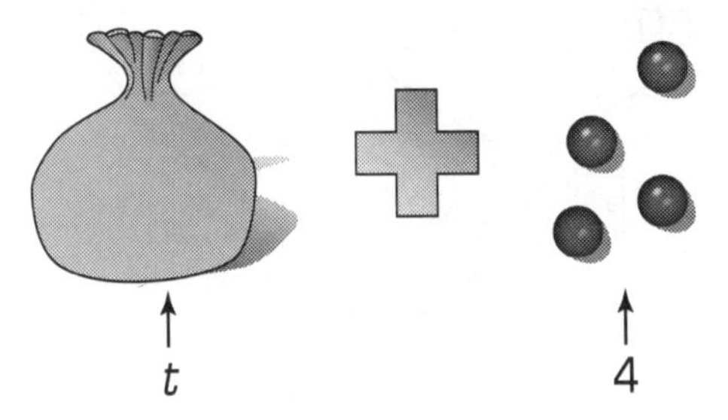

a How many marbles does Josh have altogether?
Circle the correct answer.

$t - 4$ marbles $t + 4$ marbles $4 - t$ marbles

b Josh won 6 more marbles.
How many marbles does he now have altogether?
Circle the correct answer.

$t + 4$ marbles 10 marbles $t + 10$ marbles 2 marbles

3 **a** These parcels weigh n kilograms altogether.
The small parcel to the side weighs 8 kilograms.

Add the small parcel to the big pile.
What is the total weight in kg?
Circle the correct answer.

$n + 8$ $n - 8$ $8 - n$ $n8$

b Add another parcel weighing 12 kilograms to the pile.
What is the new total weight in kg?
Circle the correct answer.

$n + 12$ 12 20 $n + 20$

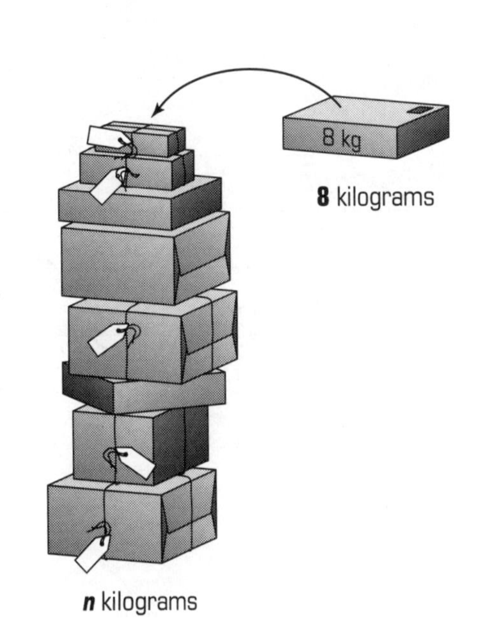

Number towers

Add the numbers in two boxes next to each other to get the number in the box below.

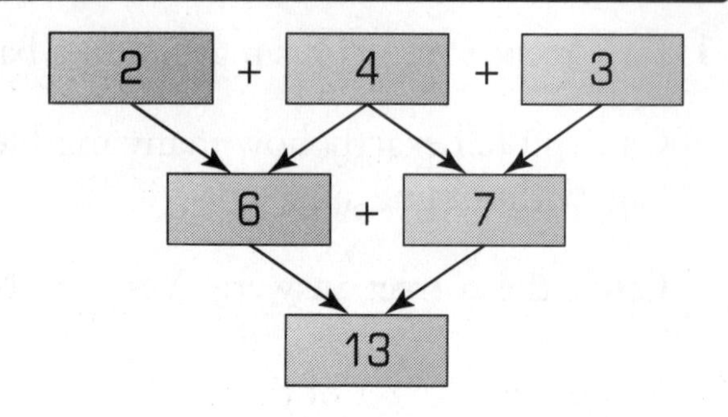

Complete these towers.

1

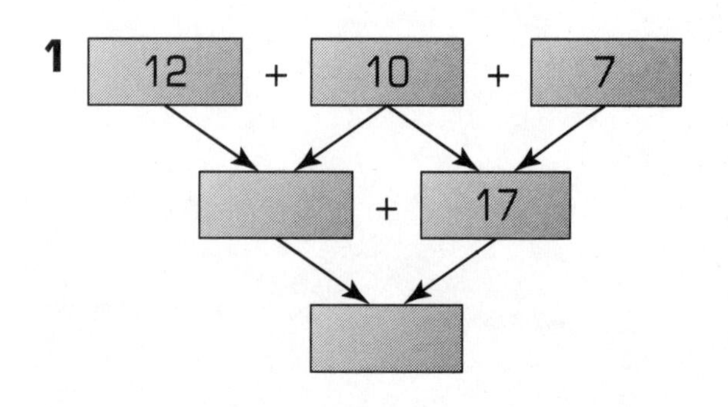

2

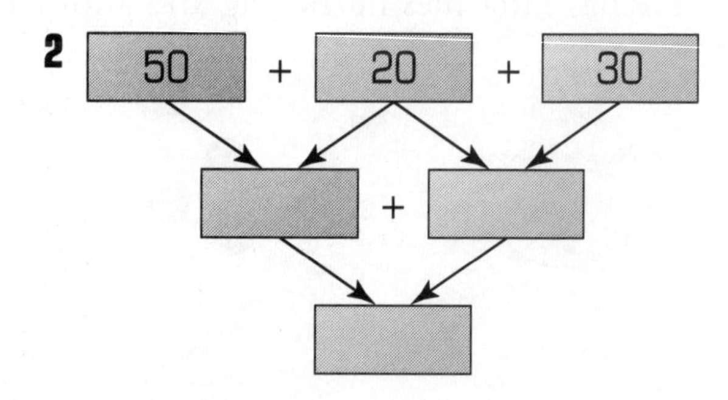

3

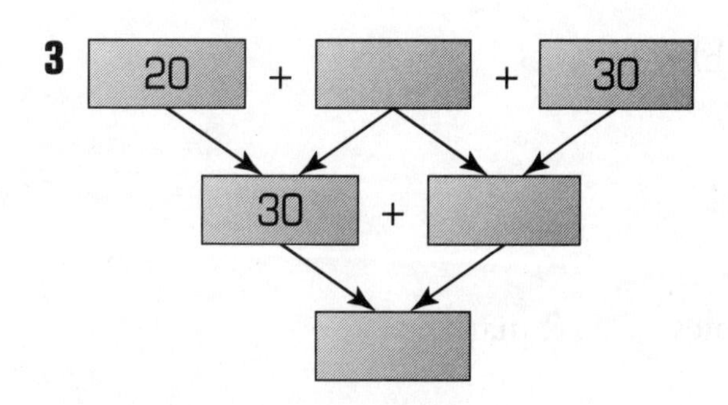

4

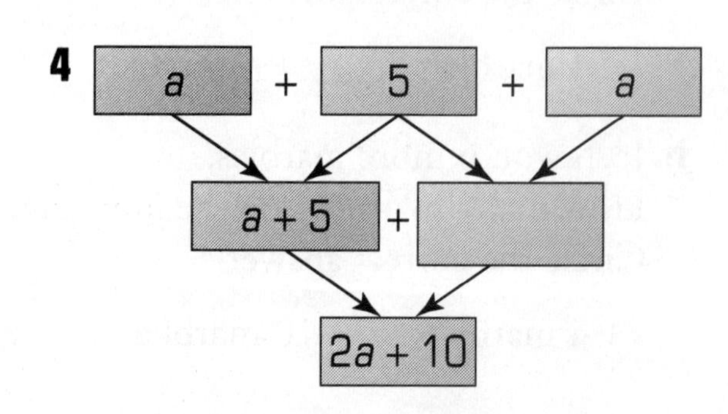

5

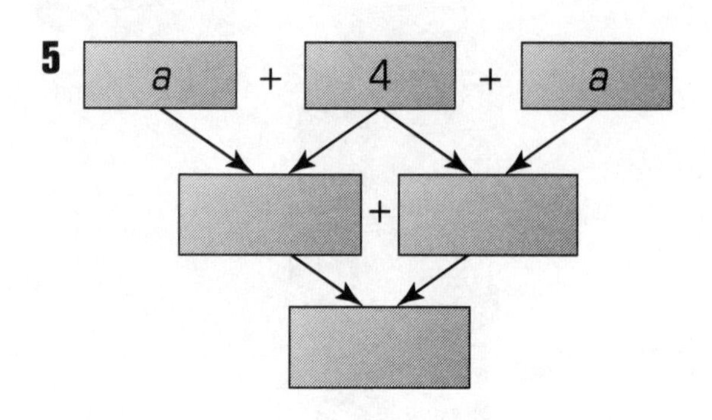

6

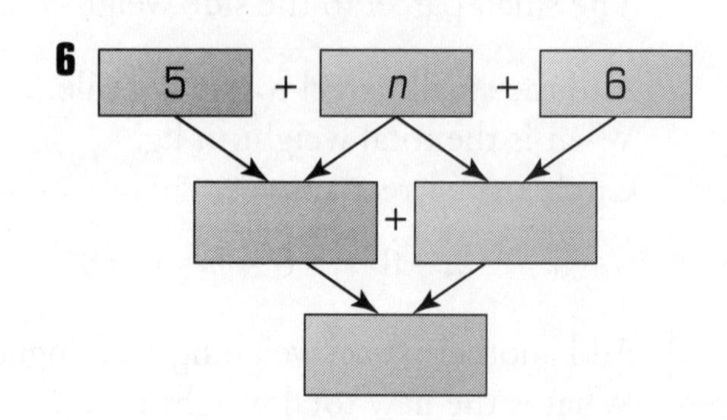

Solving algebra problems

The perimeter of a shape is the total distance around the edge.

This triangle has sides of 4 cm.
Its perimeter is 4 cm + 4 cm + 4 cm = 12 cm
You can say: 3×4 cm = 12 cm.

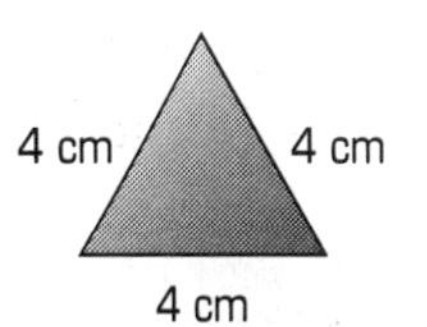

1 Find the perimeter of these shapes.

a

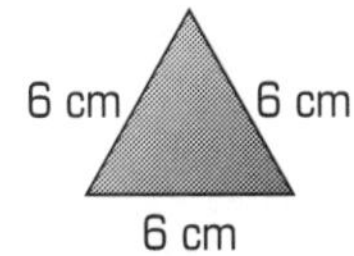

The perimeter is:

___ cm + ___ cm + ___ cm = ___ cm

Or:

___ × ___ cm = ___ cm

b

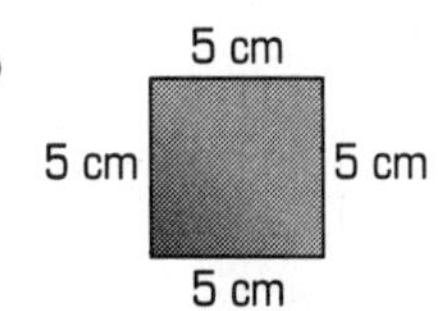

The perimeter is:

___ cm + ___ cm + ___ cm + ___ cm

= ___ cm

Or:

___ × ___ cm = ___ cm

2 In these questions the lengths of each side are written in symbols.
You can add them just like numbers.
Find the perimeter of each shape.

a

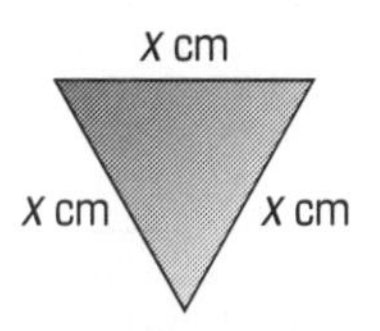

The perimeter is:

____

= _______ cm

Or:

___ × ___ cm = _______ cm

b

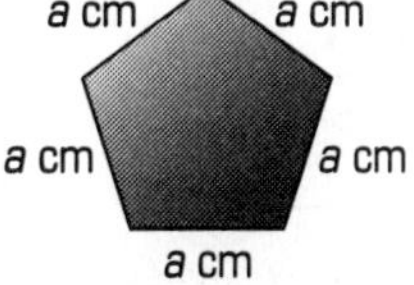
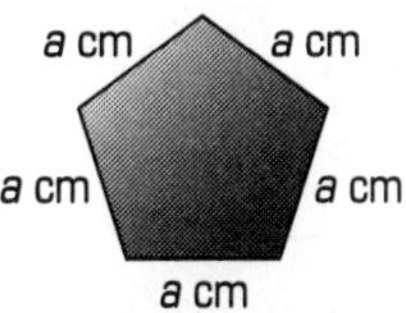

The perimeter is:

____

= _______ cm

Or:

___ × ___ cm = _______ cm

c

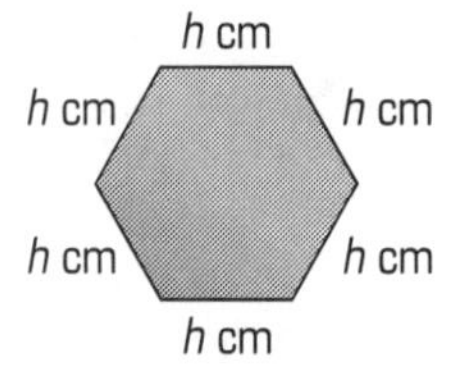

The perimeter is: ______________________ = _______ cm

Or: ___ × ___ cm = = _______ cm

Symbols and values

1 Work out the missing weights of the parcels on these scales and write them on.

a

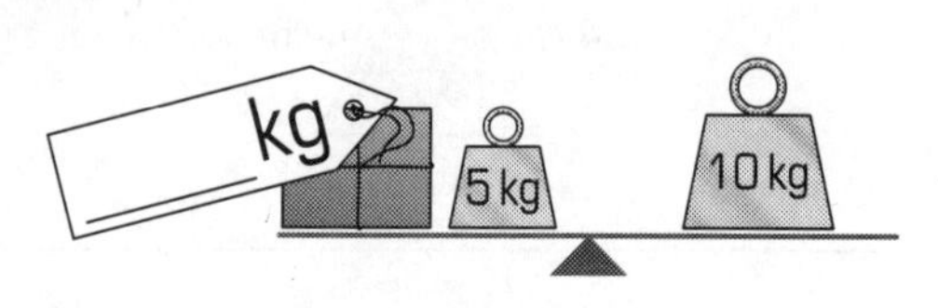

b

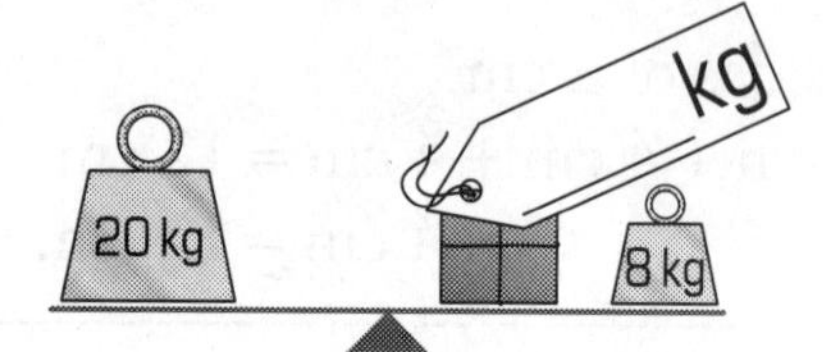

c

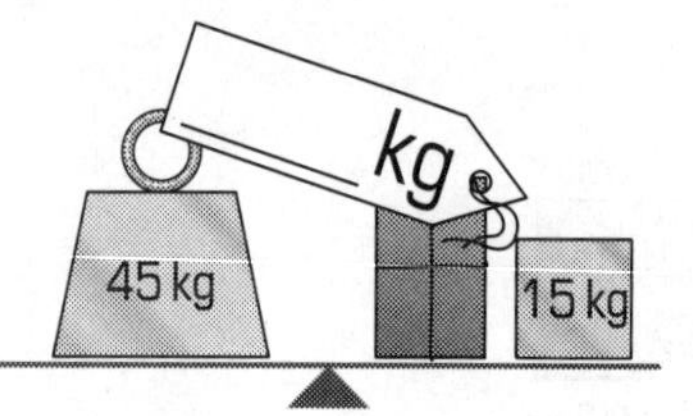

d

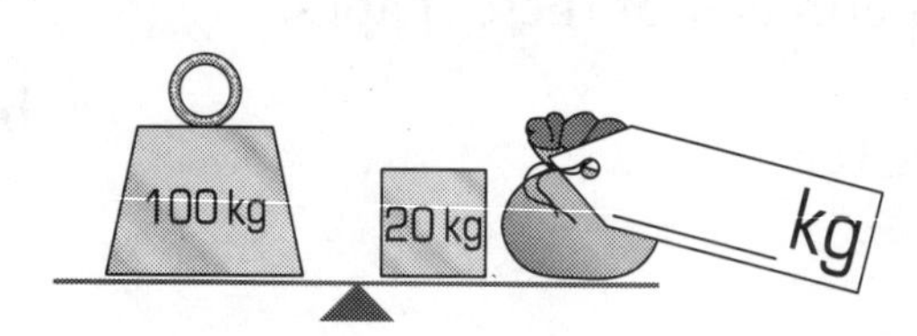

e

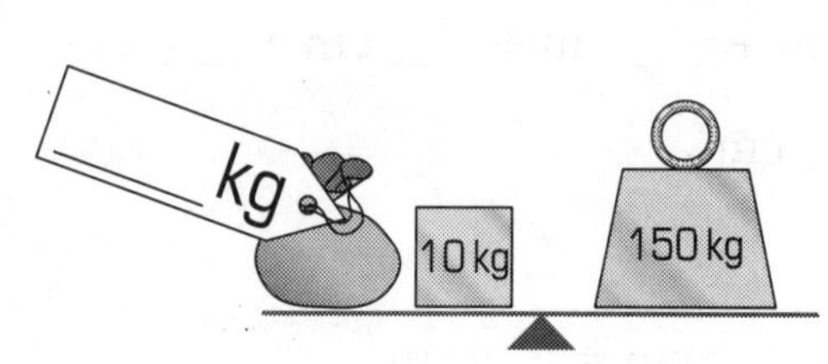

f

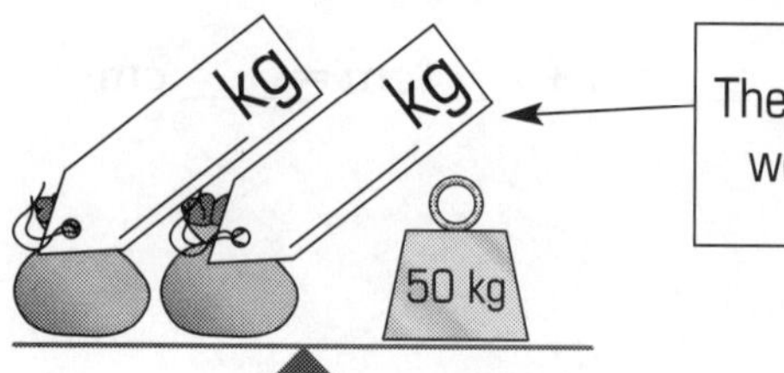

These parcels both weigh the same

2 Find the value of each letter.
The first one is done for you.

a $a + 8 = 16$

$a = 16 - 8$

$a = 8$

b $x + 9 = 12$

$x = 12 - 9$

$x =$ ___

c $15 + t = 20$

$t = 20 -$ ___

$t =$ ___

d $r + 7 = 13$

$r =$ ___ $-$ ___

$r =$ ___

e $f + 9 = 15$

$f =$ ___ $-$ ___

$f =$ ___

f $15 + p = 22$

$p =$ ___ $-$ ___

$p =$ ___

g $7 + k = 21$

$k =$ ___ $-$ ___

$k =$ ___

h $h + 10 = 35$

$h =$ ___ $-$ ___

$h =$ ___

3 In this number tower, you add two boxes to give the number in the box below.

a Fill in the missing values.

b The value of the last box is 20.
What is the value of x?

$x +$ _________ $= 20$

$x =$ _____

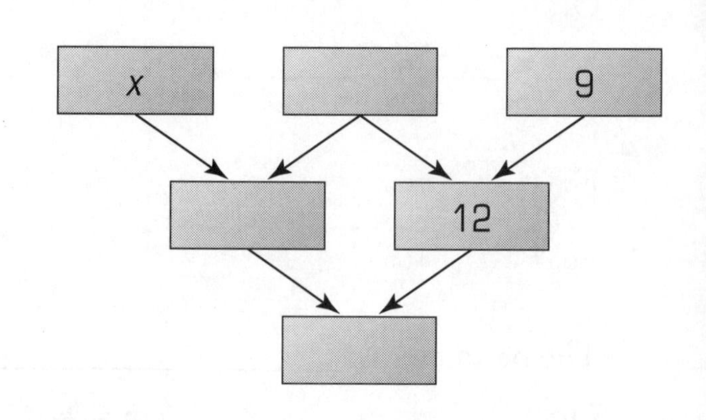

A2.5WS Substitution

Small boxes hold 3 doughnuts.

Medium boxes hold 6 doughnuts.

Large boxes hold 10 doughnuts.

You can use symbols to represent the numbers of doughnuts in each box:

$s = 3$ $m = 6$ $l = 10$

For a small box and two extra doughnuts:

$s + 2$ means $3 + 2$

so $s + 2 = 5$

1 Draw $s + 1$ doughnuts:

2 Draw $s - 2$ doughnuts:

3 Draw $m + 3$ doughnuts:

4 Draw $m - 1$ doughnuts:

5 Draw $m - 3$ doughnuts:

6 Draw $l - 3$ doughnuts:

7 Draw $s + s$ doughnuts:

8 Draw $s + m$ doughnuts:

S2.1WS Time

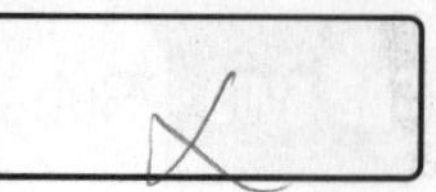

1 Put hands on each clock to show the time.

9 o'clock

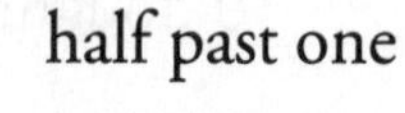

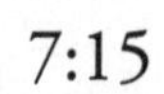

quarter to five | five past six

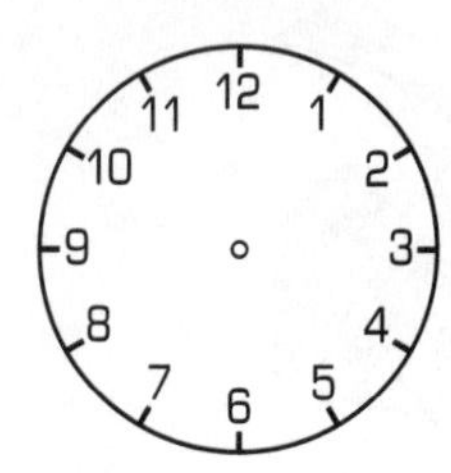
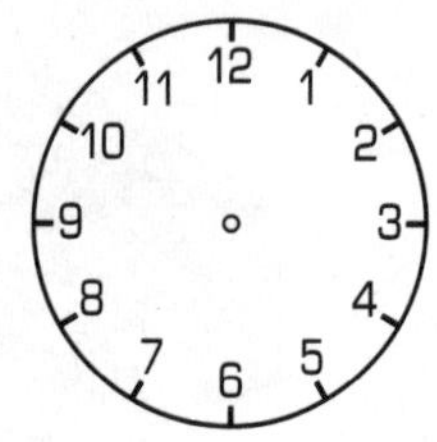
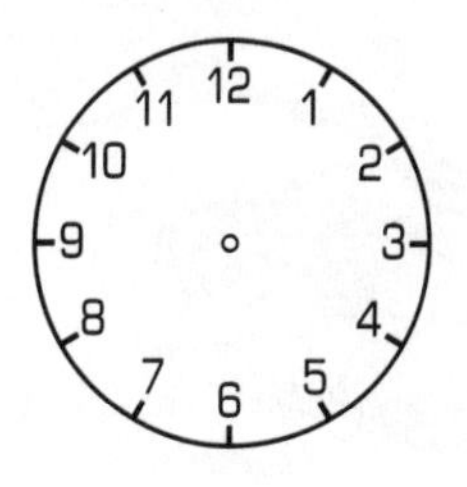
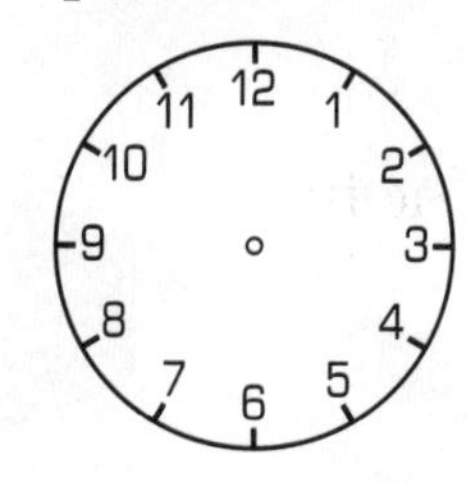
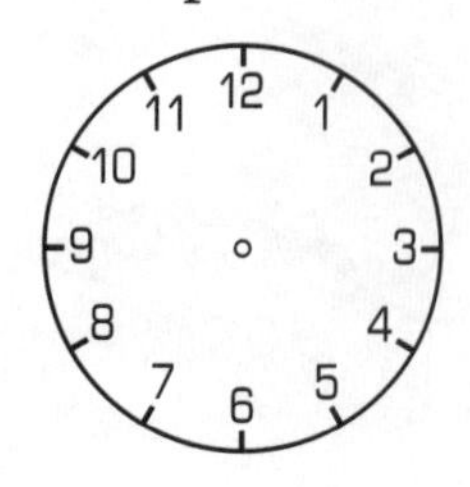

2 What times are shown on these clocks?

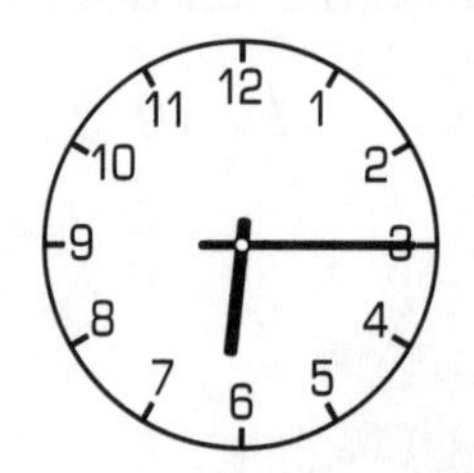

______________ ______________ ______________ ______________ ______________

This scale will help you convert between 12 and 24-hour times.

00.00	01.00	02.00	03.00	04.00	05.00	06.00	07.00	08.00	09.00	10.00	11.00	12.00	13.00	14.00	15.00	16.00	17.00	18.00	19.00	20.00	21.00	22.00	23.00	00.00
12	1 am	2 am	3 am	4 am	5 am	6 am	7 am	8 am	9 am	10 am	11 am	12	1 pm	2 pm	3 pm	4 pm	5 pm	6 pm	7 pm	8 pm	9 pm	10 pm	11 pm	12
Midnight												Midday												Midnight

am times **pm times**

3 Put hands on each clock to show these 24-hour times. Use the scale to help you.

07:30 | 10:00 | 13:30 | 16:45 | 23:30

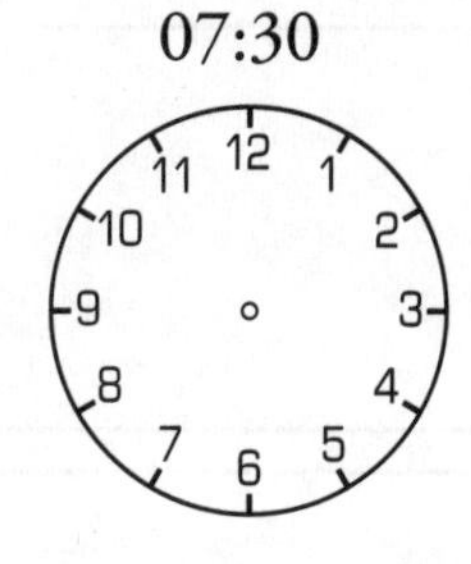
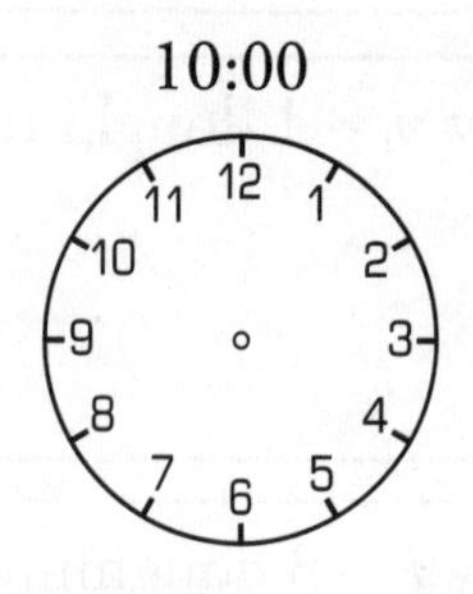
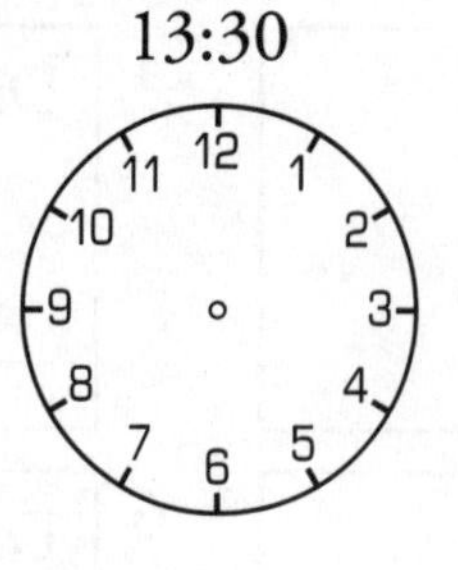
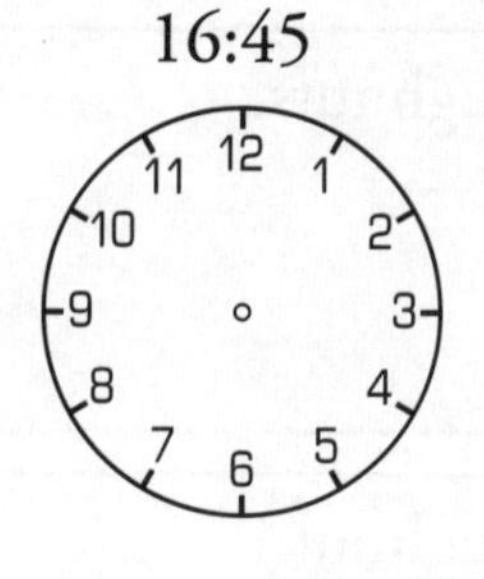
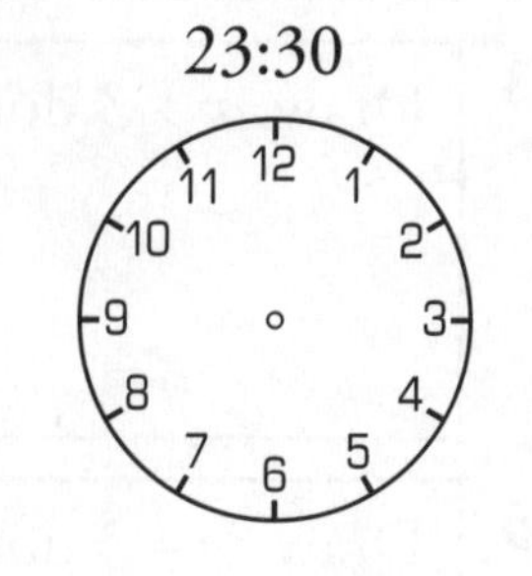

4 Convert these 12-hour times to 24-hour times. Use the scale to help you.

a 9.30 am → __________ **b** 8.00 am → __________ **c** 8.00 pm → __________

d 2.30 pm → __________ **e** 1.30 am → __________ **f** 11.00 pm → __________

5 Convert these 24-hour times to 12-hour times. Use the scale to help you.

a 09:00 hrs → __________ **b** 16:00 hrs → __________ **c** 03:31 hrs → __________

d 21:35 hrs → __________ **e** 11:32 hrs → __________ **f** 23:36 hrs → __________

 Reading coordinates

Franco goes on a journey. Here is a map of the area.

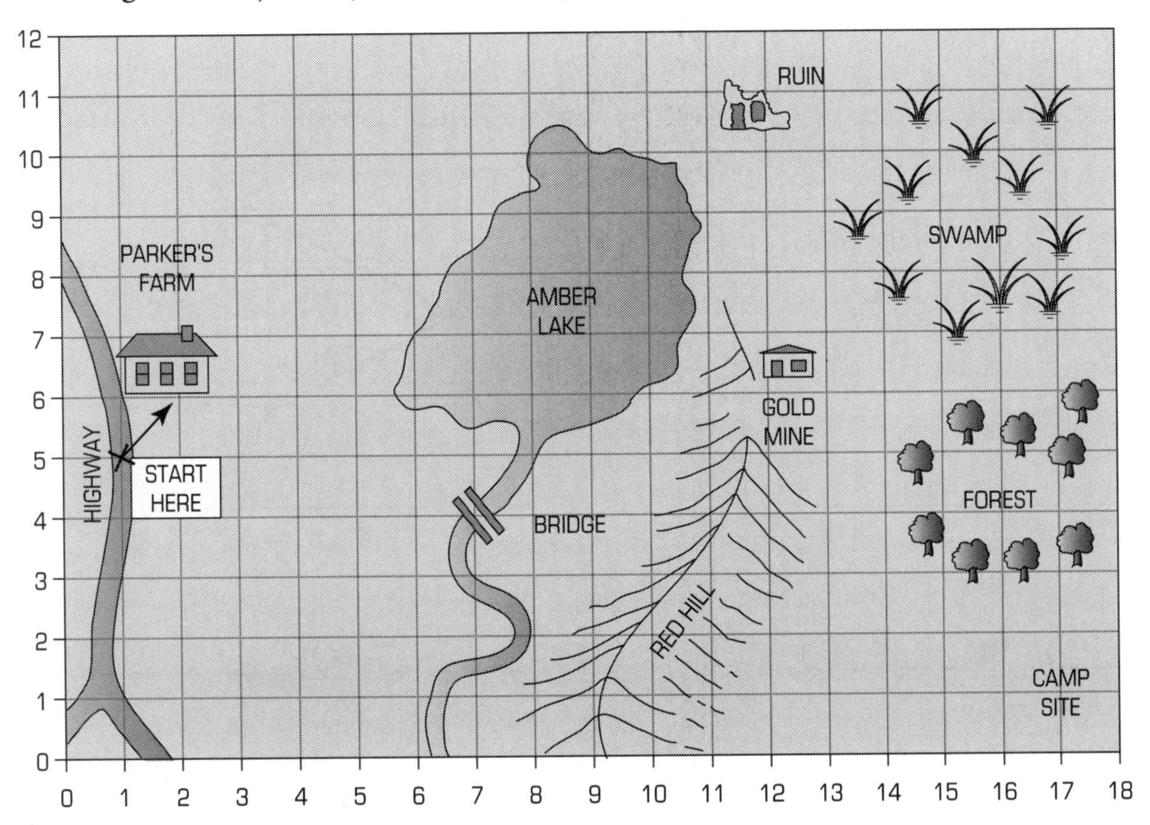

1 Plot the points and join them on the map to show Franco's journey.

(1, 5) (3, 7) (8, 11) (11, 10) (11, 8) (13, 7)

(14, 5) (14, 3) (15, 2) (17, 1)

Remember, you go **across** first, then **up**.

2 What will Franco see on his left at (3, 7)? ______________

3 What will Franco see on his right at (11, 10)? ______________

4 What will Franco see on his left at (11, 10)? ______________

5 What will Franco see on his right at (13, 7)? ______________

6 What will Franco see on his left at (15, 2)? ______________

7 Plot a shorter route from the Highway (1, 5) to the Camp Site (17, 1). Draw the new route on the map, and write the co-ordinates here.

____

____

S2.3WS Coordinates and shapes

1 a Write the coordinates of the points A, B and C.

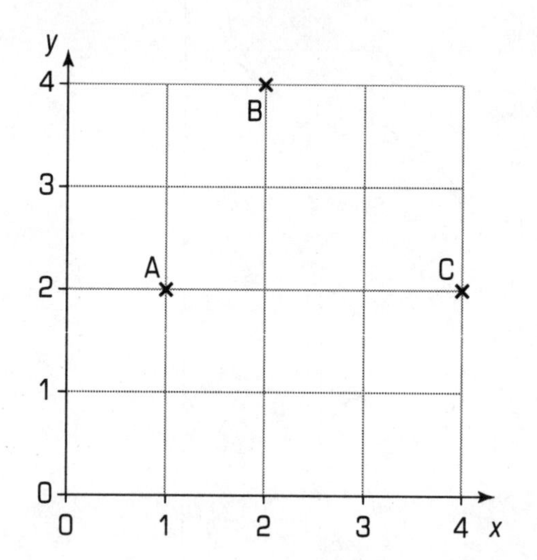

A(____, ____) B(____, ____)

C(____, ____)

b Write the coordinates of the points P, Q and R.

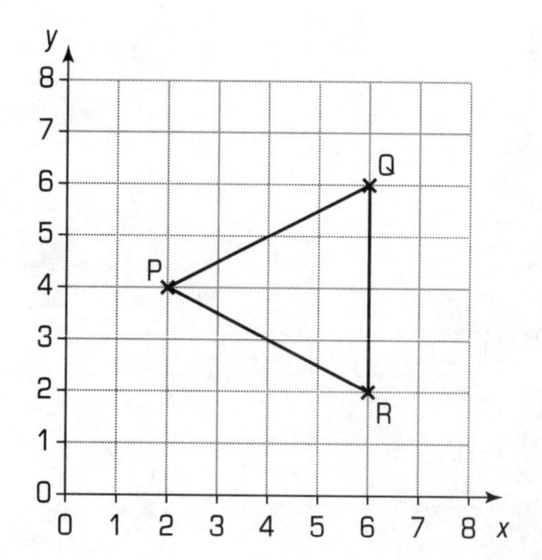

P(____, ____) Q(____, ____)

R(____, ____)

2 a Plot these points on this grid.

(5, 3) (5, 6) (5, 9) (1, 6) (14, 6)

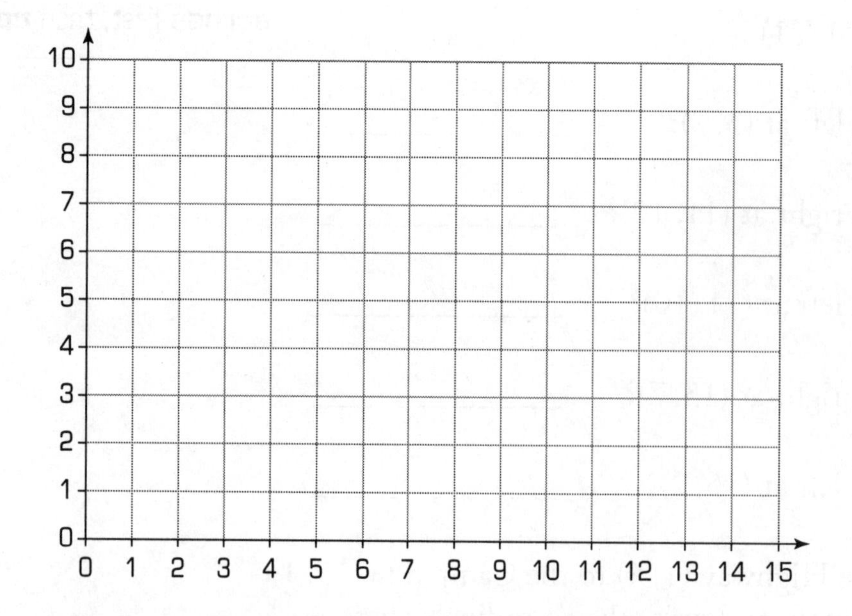

b Join all the points together with straight lines.

c What shape have you drawn? ______________

Sorting

1 Sort these 20 words onto the four lists.

hammer France Emily blue Ann Canada
hack-saw green brown James China yellow John
drill Egypt purple Alfie spade Pakistan pliers

Colours	Names	Tools	Countries

2 Sort the numbers 1–9 onto this Carroll diagram.

1 2 3
4 5 6
7 8 9

	Straight lines only	Has curved lines
Odd number		
Even number		

3 Sort the shapes onto the Venn diagram.

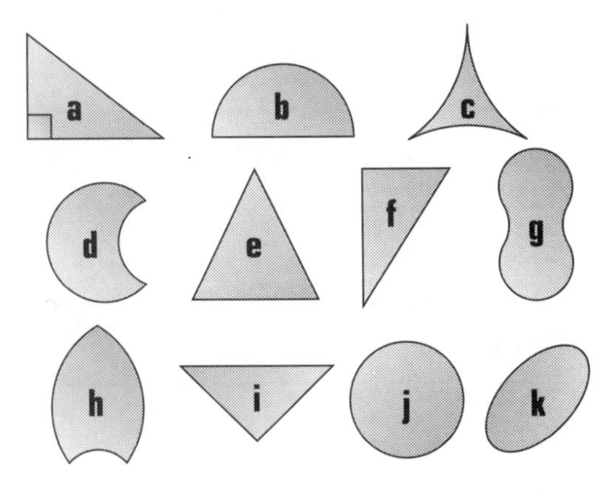

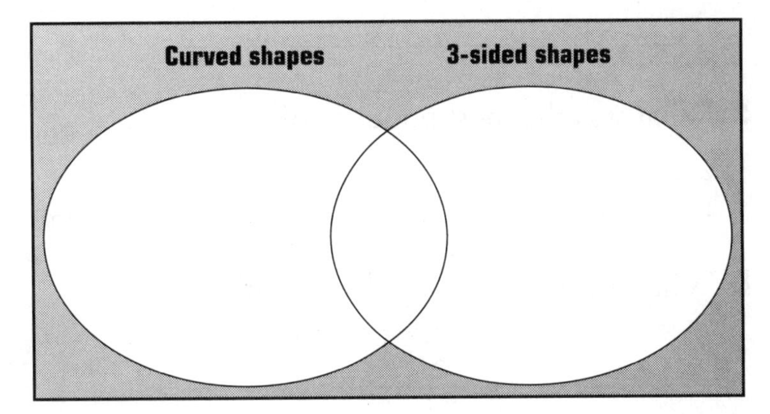

D2.4WS Displaying data

Class 7P call out their favourite colours for a survey.

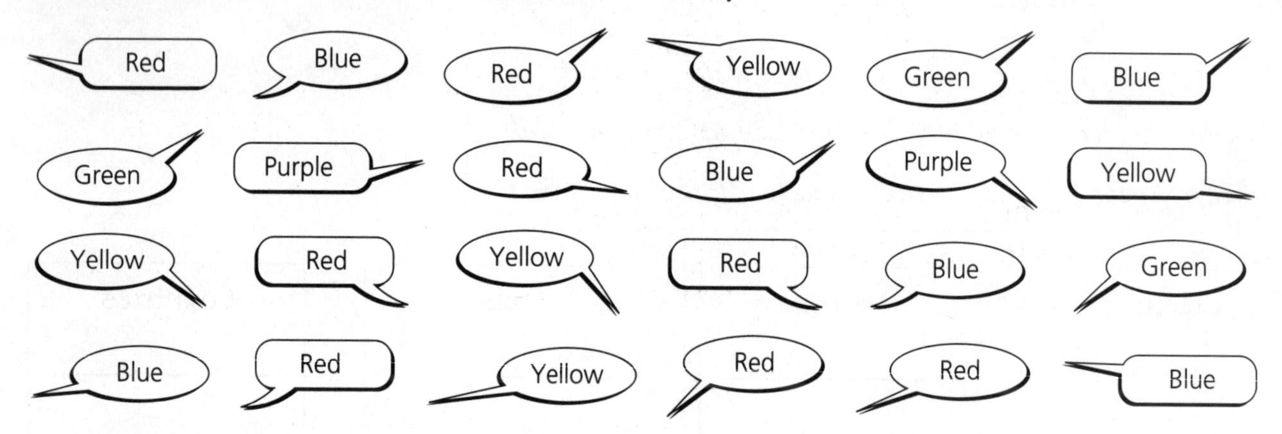

1 Tally the data from this survey into this table.

2 Write the totals in the frequency column.

Colour	Tally	Frequency
Blue		
Green		
Purple		
Red		
Yellow		

3 Complete this pictogram to show this data.
Use ☺ to represent one person.

Favourite colour

Blue	
Green	
Purple	
Red	
Yellow	
	Number of students

Key: ☺ = ___________

4 How many students called out Blue?

____

5 What was the most popular colour?

____

6 What was the least popular colour?

____

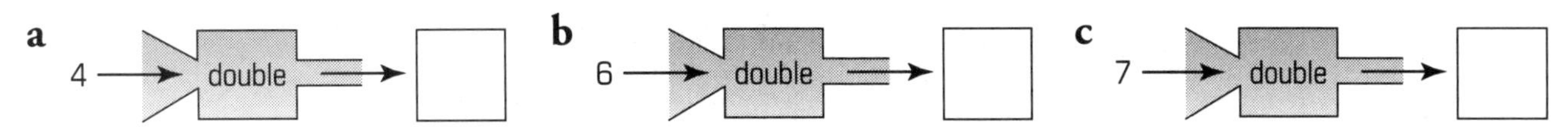

N3.2WS Mental multiplication

1 Double these numbers. Write your answers in the boxes.

a 4 → double → ☐ **b** 6 → double → ☐ **c** 7 → double → ☐

2 Double each of the numbers in the 'arrow' boxes.
Write your answers in the circles.

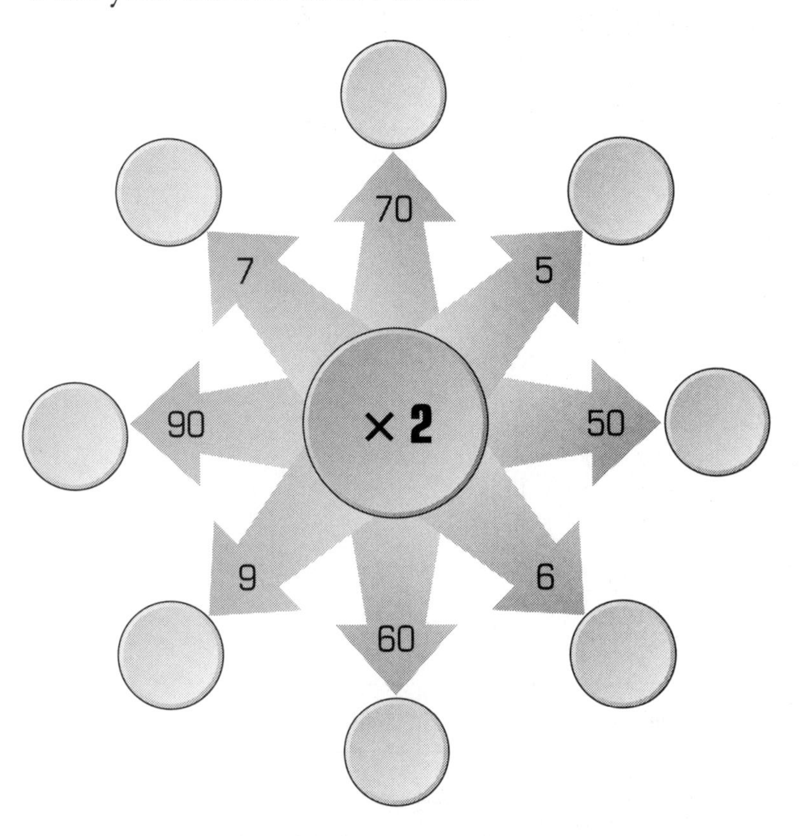

3 Multiply the numbers in these boxes by 20.
First double them, then multiply by 10.

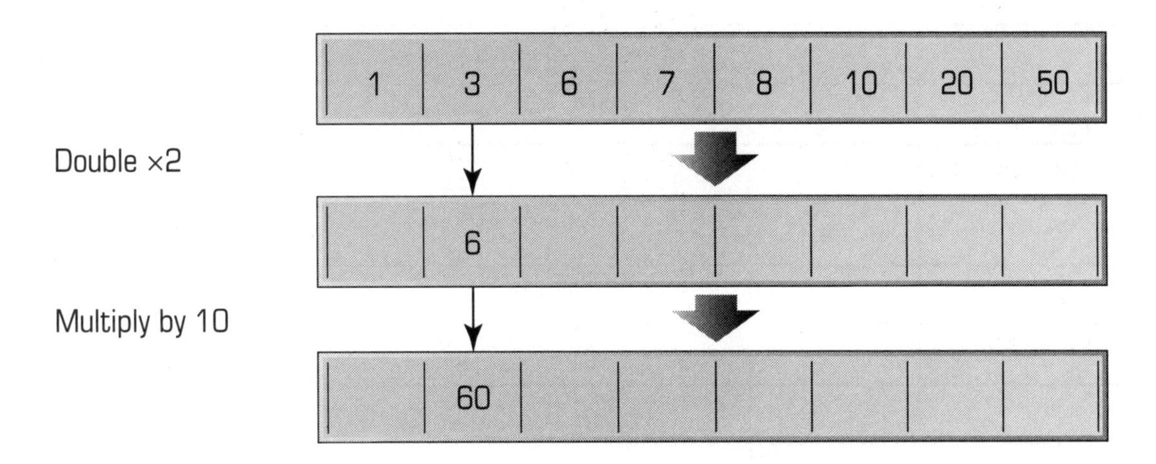

Multiplying decimals by 10

1 Draw lines of these lengths on the rulers.

a 3.4 cm

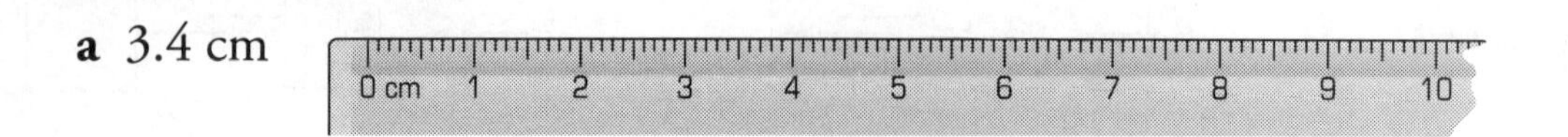

b 6.7 cm

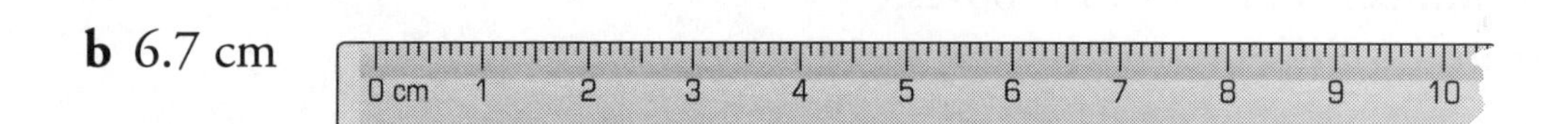

c 9.1 cm

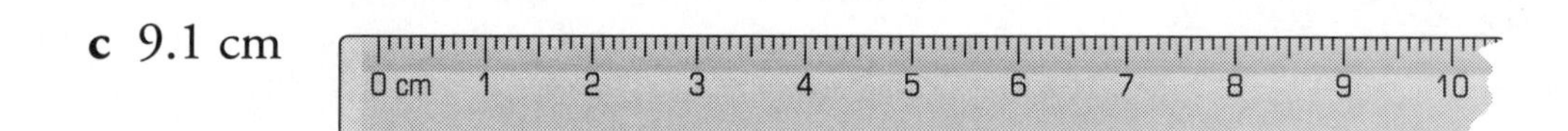

2 When you multiply a number by 10 you move the digits one place to the left.

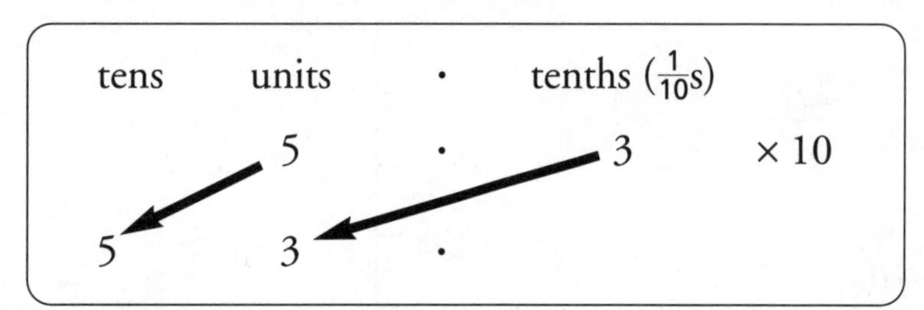

Multiply these numbers by 10. Write your answers in the table.

	calculation	hundreds	tens	units	·	tenths ($\frac{1}{10}$s)
a				2	·	5
	2.5 × 10 =				·	
b				5	·	2
	5.2 × 10 =				·	
c				7	·	0
	7.0 × 10 =				·	
d					·	
	12.7 × 10 =				·	
e					·	
	20.9 × 10 =				·	
f					·	
	0.8 × 10 =				·	

N3.4WS Dividing whole numbers by 10

When you divide a number by 10, you move the digits one place to the right.

hundreds	tens	units	
3	2	0	÷ 10
	3	2	

Divide these numbers by 10. Move the digits one place to the right.
The first one is done for you.

	calculation	hundreds	tens	units
1			9	0
	90 ÷ 10 =			9
2			3	0
	30 ÷ 10 =			
3				
	50 ÷ 10 =			
4				
	120 ÷ 10 =			
5				
	170 ÷ 10 =			
6				
	230 ÷ 10 =			
7				
	540 ÷ 10 =			
8				
	860 ÷ 10 =			
9				
	490 ÷ 10 =			
10				
	800 ÷ 10 =			

1 Multiply these numbers by 10:

a 7 × 10 = ________ **b** 15 × 10 = ________

c 23 × 10 = ________ **d** 47 × 10 = ________

e 56 × 10 = ________ **f** 98 × 10 = ________

2 Rewrite these measurements in centimetres or millimetres.

10 mm = 1 cm 100 cm = 1 m

Do not try to measure the drawings, they are not accurate.

a

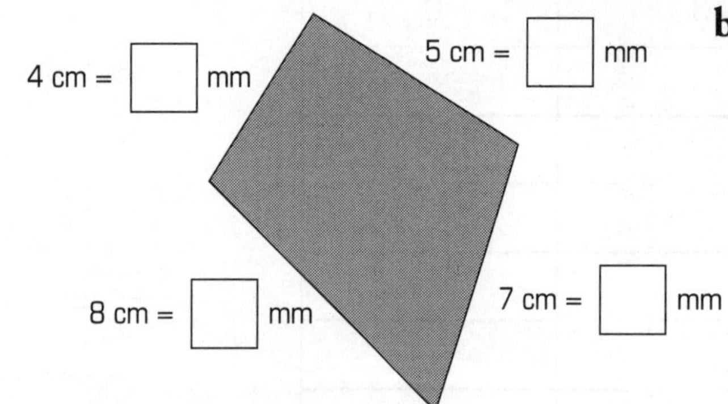

b

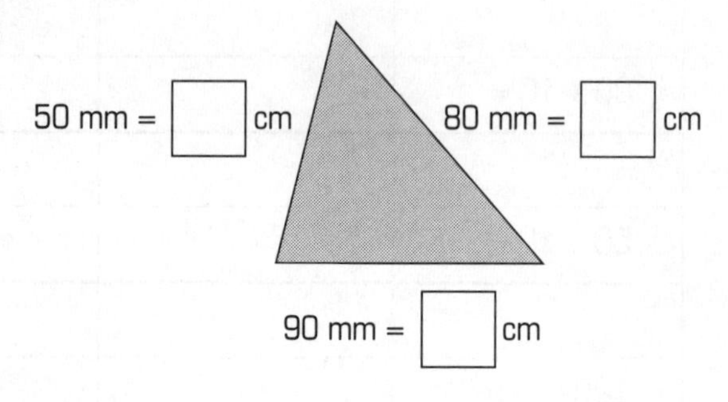

c

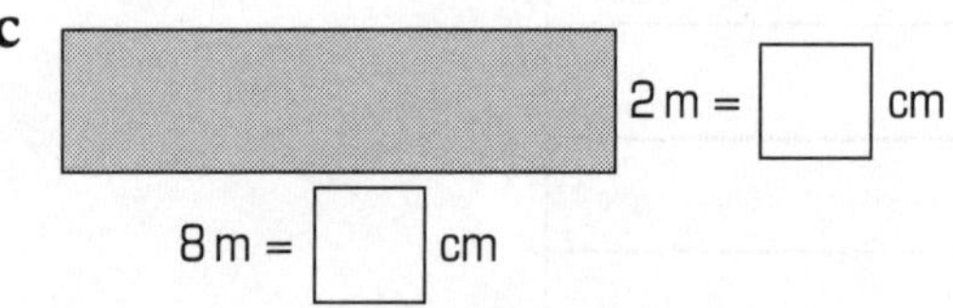

3 Use these signs, > or <, between the pairs of measurements to make these statements true.

a 60 mm ☐ 7 cm **b** 2 m ☐ 120 cm

c 250 mm ☐ 20 cm **d** 3 m ☐ 400 m

e 5 m ☐ 60 cm **f** 34 mm ☐ 5 cm

Multiplying by partitioning

1 Complete these calculations.

a $2 \times 4 =$ ______ **b** $3 \times 6 =$ ______ **c** $5 \times 6 =$ ______

d $8 \times 7 =$ ______ **e** $5 \times 4 =$ ______ **f** $6 \times 8 =$ ______

g ______ $\times 4 = 16$ **h** $3 \times$ ______ $= 24$ **i** ______ $\times 4 = 36$

2 Split up these numbers into tens and units.

a 16 is the same as [10] + [ ]

b 11 is the same as [10] + [ ]

c 19 is the same as [10] + [ ]

d 13 is the same as [10] + [ ]

3 Fill in the boxes to multiply these numbers.

a 16×4

16 is [10] + [ ]

$10 \times 4 =$ [ ]

$6 \times 4 =$ [ ]

So $16 \times 4 =$ [40] + [ ]

= [ ]

b 19×3

19 is [ ] + [9]

$10 \times 3 =$ [ ]

$9 \times 3 =$ [ ]

So $19 \times 3 =$ [ ] + [ ]

= [ ]

c 15×7

15 is [10] + [ ]

$10 \times 7 =$ [ ]

$5 \times 7 =$ [ ]

So $15 \times 7 =$ [ ] + [ ]

= [ ]

d 14×4

14 is [ ] + [ ]

$10 \times 4 =$ [ ]

$4 \times 4 =$ [ ]

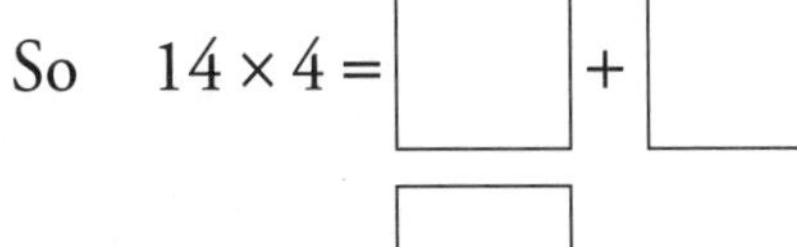

So $14 \times 4 =$ [ ] + [ ]

= [ ]

Division on a number line

Use these number lines to work out these divisions.
The number lines are marked to help you.

1 $32 \div 4 =$ ☐

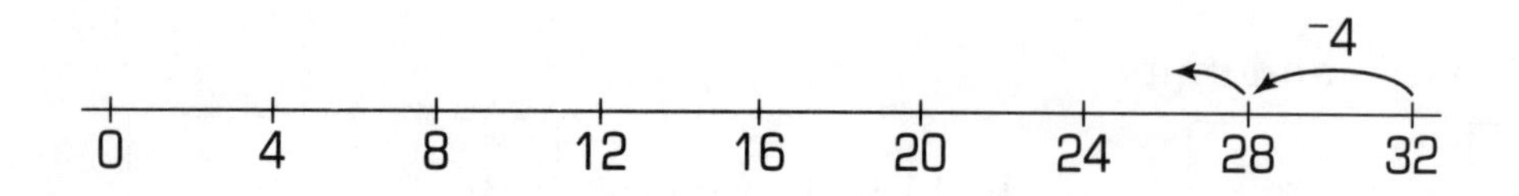

Jump backwards until you reach 0

2 $40 \div 5 =$ ☐

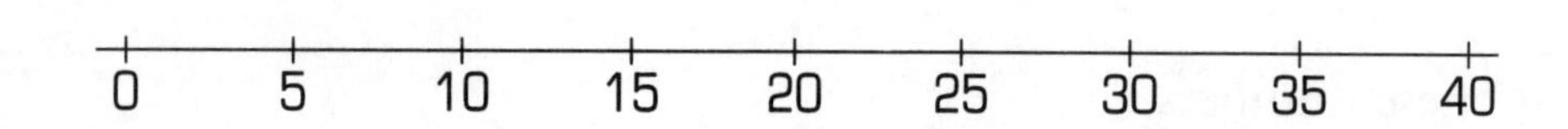

3 $27 \div 3 =$ ☐

Be careful where you start.

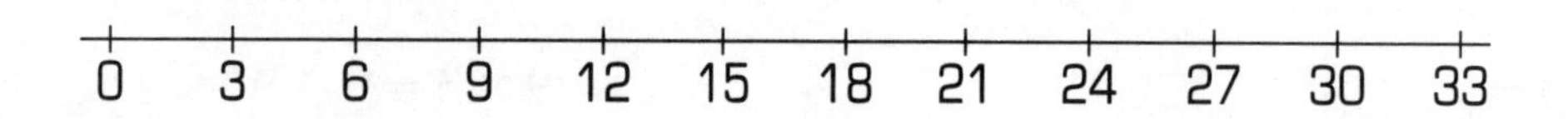

4 $25 \div 5 =$ ☐

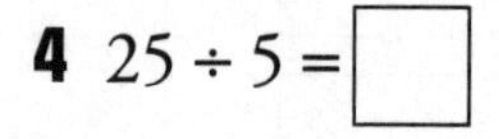

Write your own numbers on the line.
Count down in 5s.

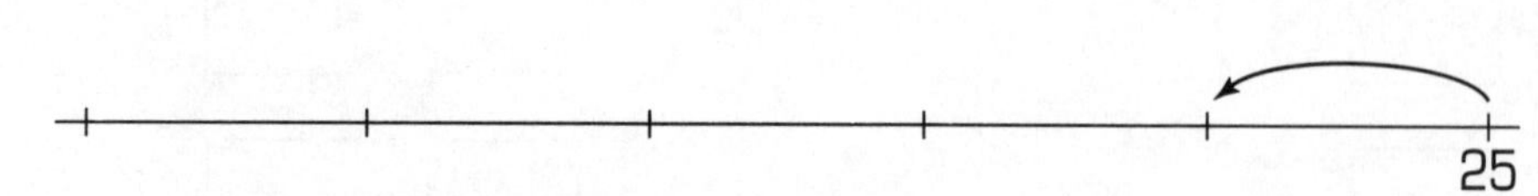

5 $48 \div 4 =$ ☐

Write your own numbers on the line.
Start at 48 and count down in 4s.

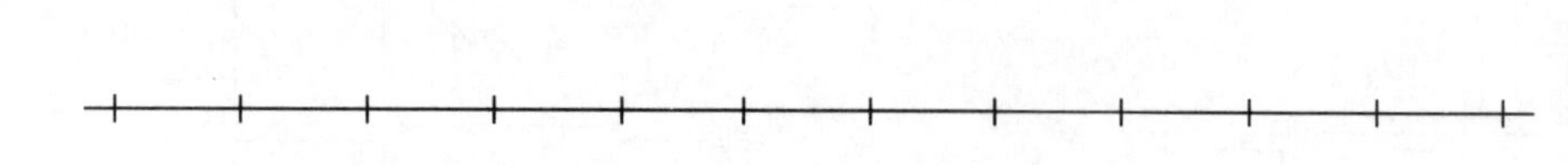

N3.8WS More division ideas

Use this multiplication table to help you to divide by doubling.

- The number in the circle is **half** the first number in the calculation.
- Fill in the circles and complete the 'halve it' sums.
- **Double** the answers in the squares, and write them in the triangles.
- This is the answer to the calculation.

×	1	2	3	4	5	6	7	8	9	10
1	1	2	3	4	5	6	7	8	9	10
2	2	4	6	8	10	12	14	16	18	20
3	3	6	9	12	15	18	21	24	27	30
4	4	8	12	16	20	24	28	32	36	40
5	5	10	15	20	25	30	35	40	45	50
6	6	12	18	24	30	36	42	48	54	60
7	7	14	21	28	35	42	49	56	63	70
8	8	16	24	32	40	48	56	64	72	80
9	9	18	27	36	45	54	63	72	81	90
10	10	20	30	40	50	60	70	80	90	100

	calculation	halve it			double it	
1	54 ÷ 3	27	÷ 3 =	9	54 ÷ 3 =	18
2	90 ÷ 5	45	÷ 5 =		90 ÷ 5 =	
3	126 ÷ 7	63	÷ 7 =		126 ÷ 7 =	
4	84 ÷ 6		÷ 6 =		84 ÷ 6 =	
5	108 ÷ 9		÷ 9 =		108 ÷ 9 =	
6	96 ÷ 8		÷ 8 =		96 ÷ 8 =	
7	96 ÷ 6		÷ 6 =		96 ÷ 6 =	
8	72 ÷ 4		÷ 4 =		72 ÷ 4 =	
9	36 ÷ 2		÷ 2 =		36 ÷ 2 =	
10	126 ÷ 9		÷ 9 =		126 ÷ 9 =	
11	98 ÷ 7		÷ 7 =		98 ÷ 7 =	
12	144 ÷ 8		÷ 8 =		144 ÷ 8 =	

Factors

You can arrange these 10 counters into two rectangle patterns.

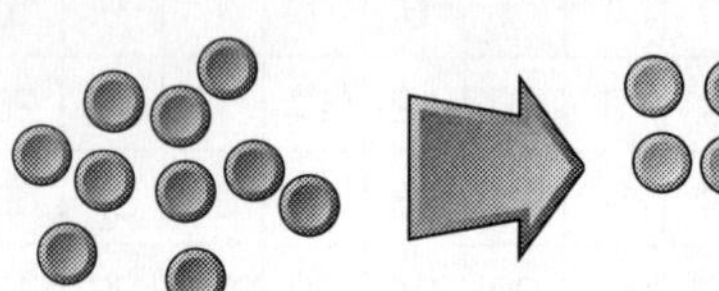 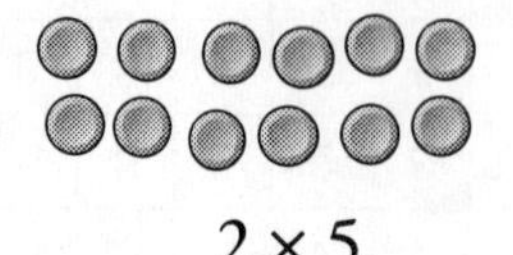 or 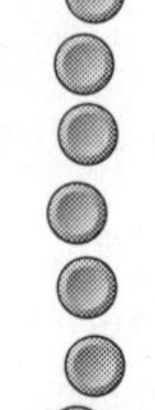

2×5 10×1

$10 = 2 \times 5$ and 1×10
1, 2, 5 and 10 are **factors** of 10.

1 a Arrange these 12 counters into 3 different rectangle patterns on this grid:

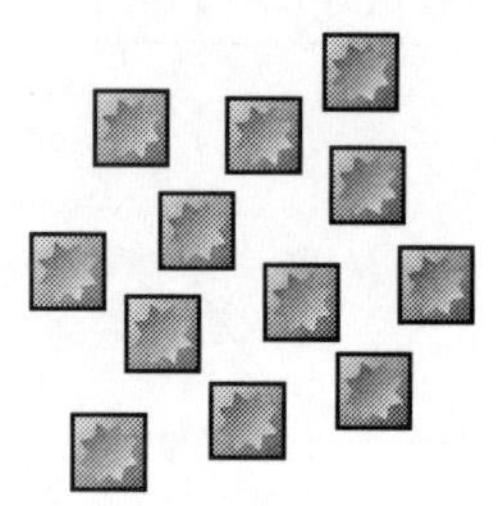

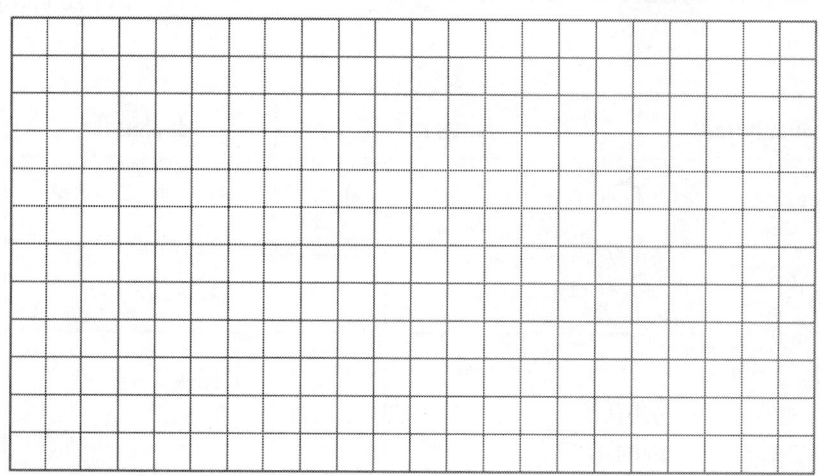

b List all the factors of 12: ______________________

2 a There are 18 counters here.
Draw rectangle patterns to list all the factors of 18.

There are 3 different rectangle patterns.

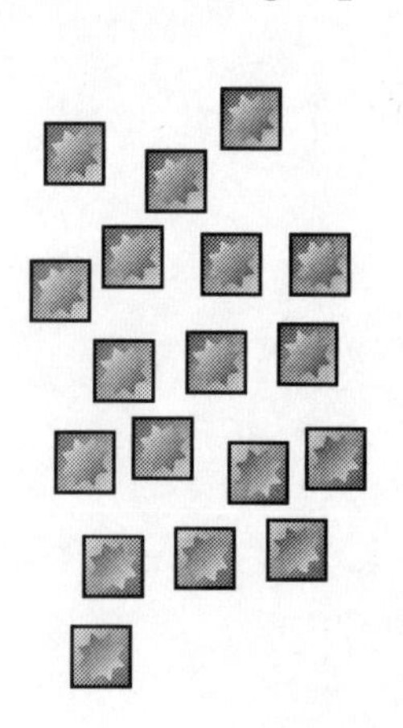

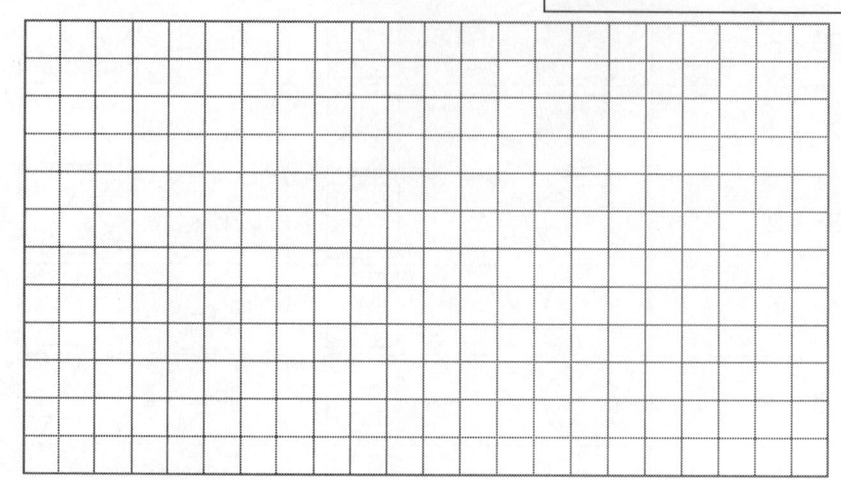

b List all the factors of 18: ______________________

1 Multiply the numbers in the arrow boxes by 3.
Write your answers in the circles.

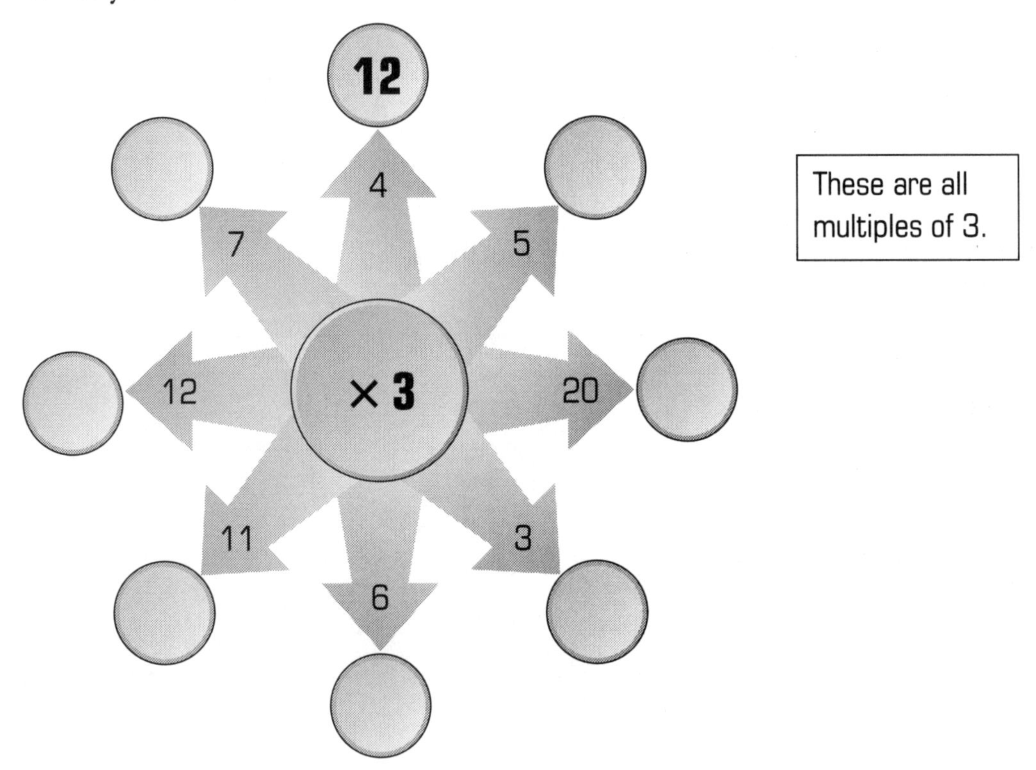

These are all multiples of 3.

2 Use question 1 to help you multiply each number by 30.
Write your answers in the circles.

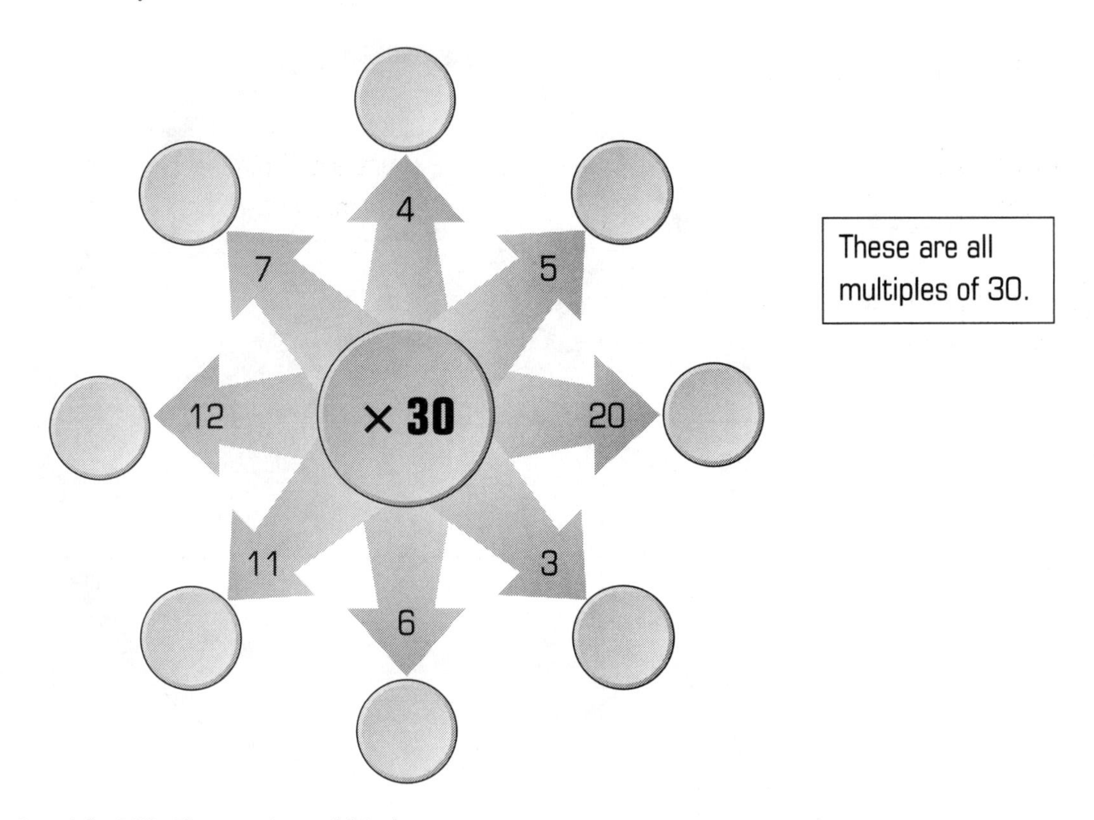

These are all multiples of 30.

Multiplication mappings

The relationship between the **before** and **after** numbers is add 2:

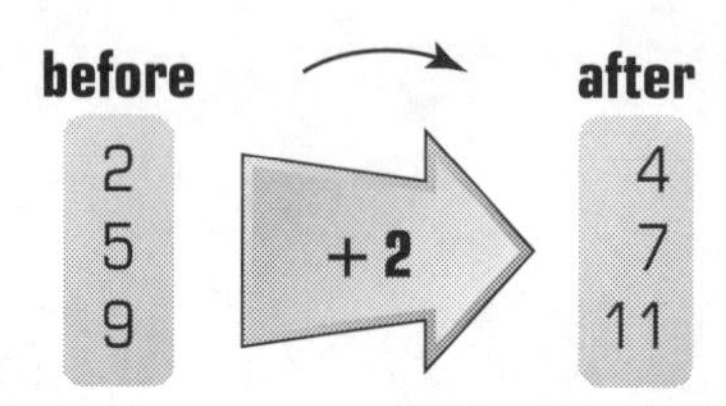

1 Write the relationship between the **before** and **after** numbers.

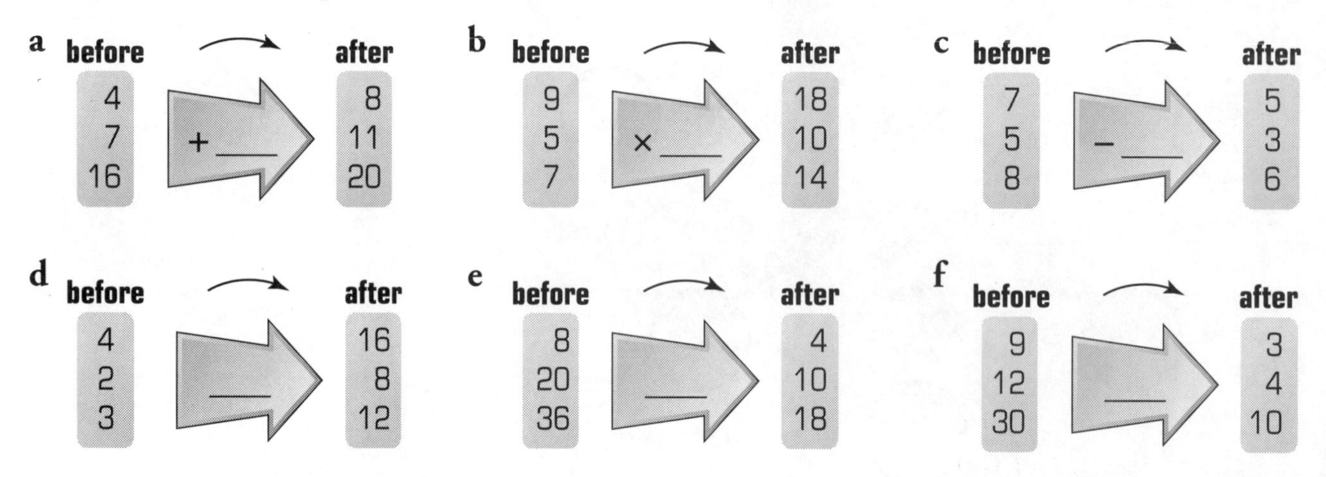

2 This drawing shows an ant and its enlargement in a microscope.

a Measure the lengths of the two images.

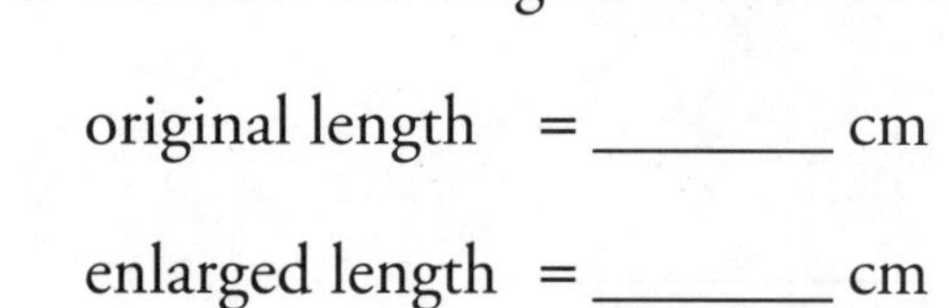

original length = ________ cm

enlarged length = ________ cm

b What is the relationship that describes the enlargement?

Answer: ____________.

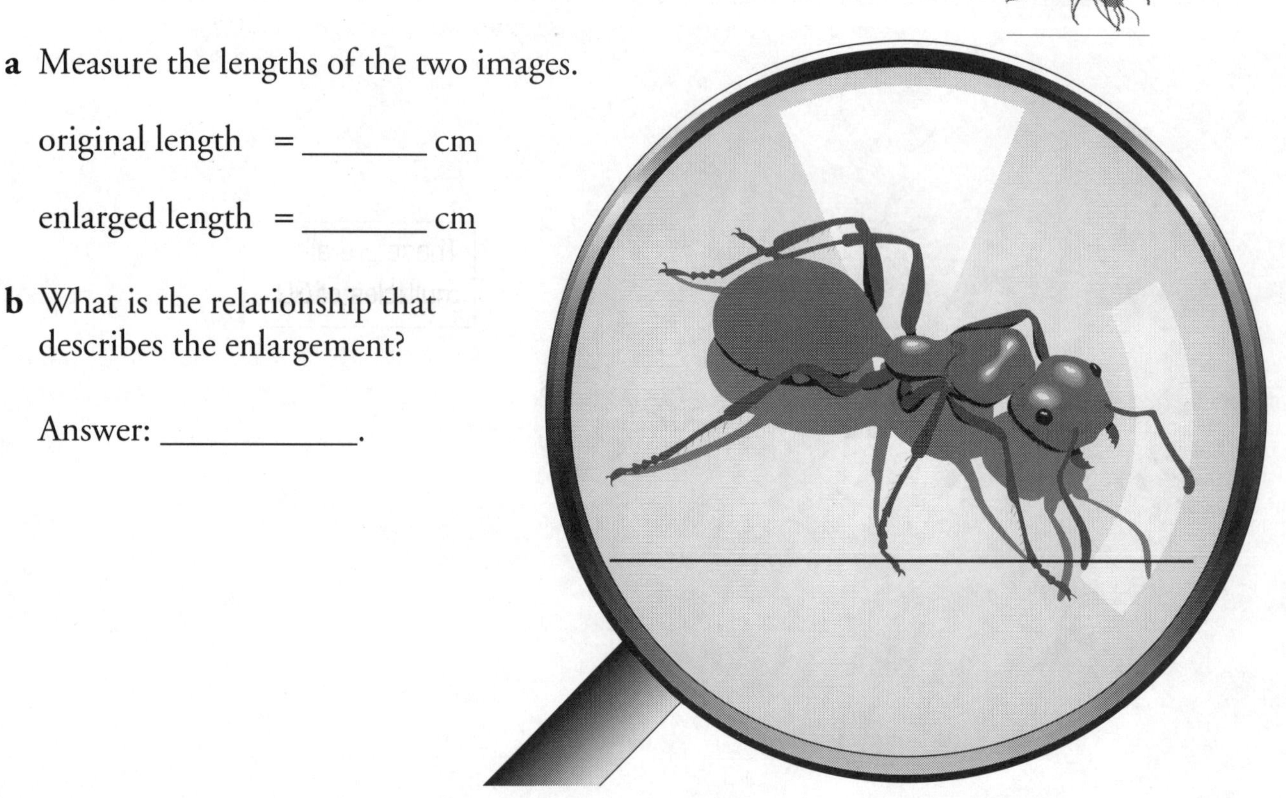

A3.5WS Plotting pairs

1 **a** Write these mapping pairs as coordinates.

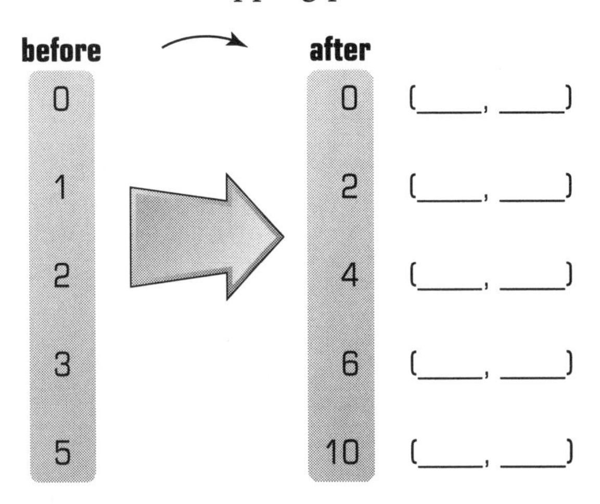

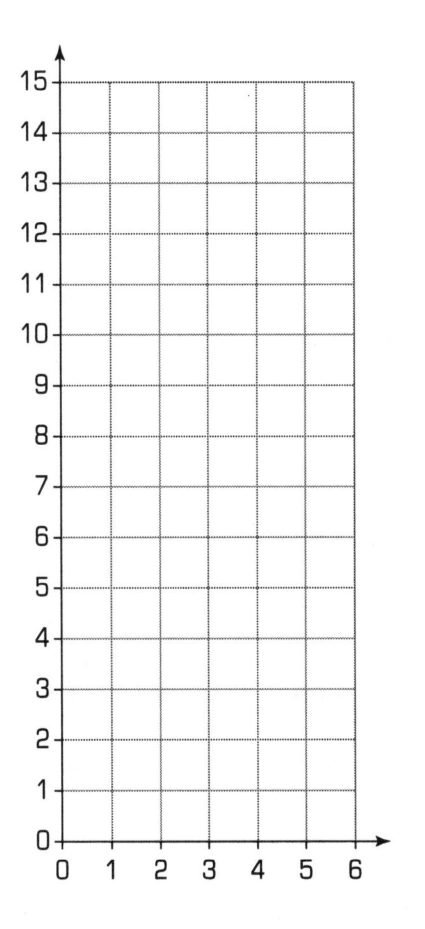

b Plot the points on this grid.

c Join the points with a straight line.
Use a ruler.

d Write the rule that connects the **before** and **after** numbers.

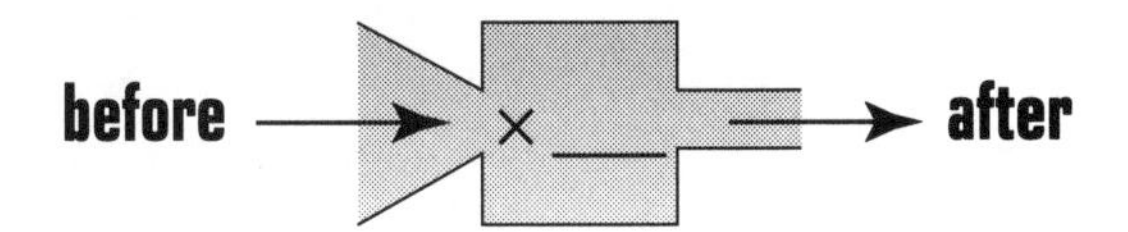

e Fill in these mapping pairs from the graph:

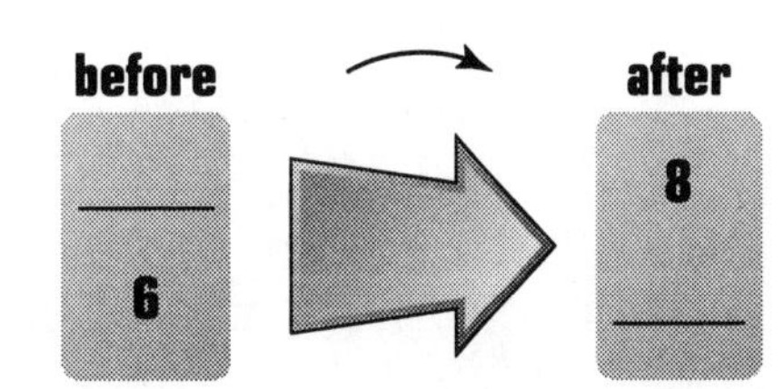

2 **a** Complete the mapping by filling in the **after** values from the graph.

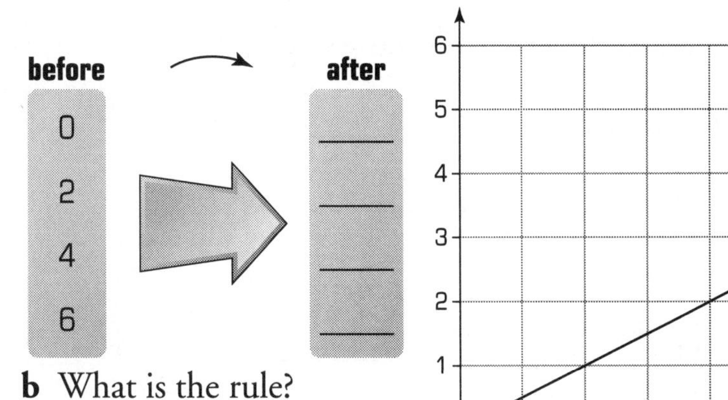

b What is the rule?

____

S3.1WS Compass turns

1 Fill in the missing points on this compass.

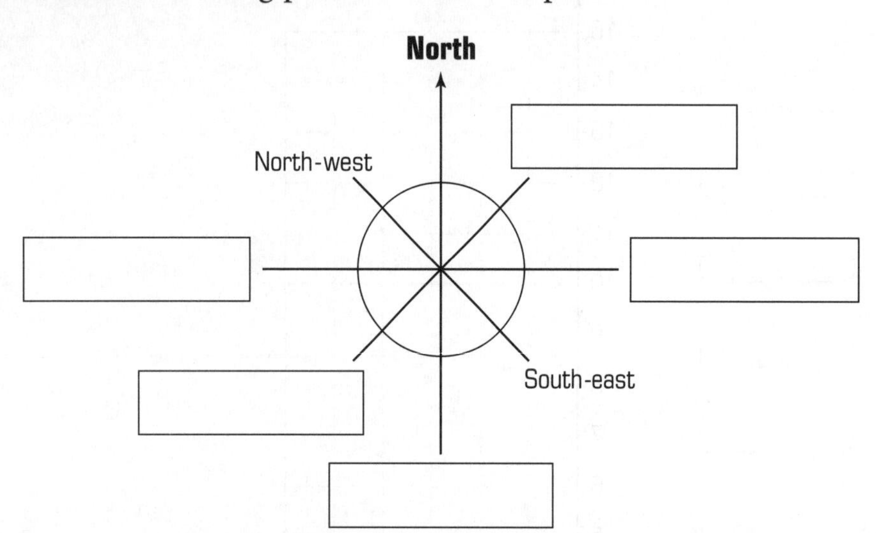

Choose your answers from this box:

South-west East
North-east
South West

2 a Fill in each new direction of this journey. Start at 'North'.

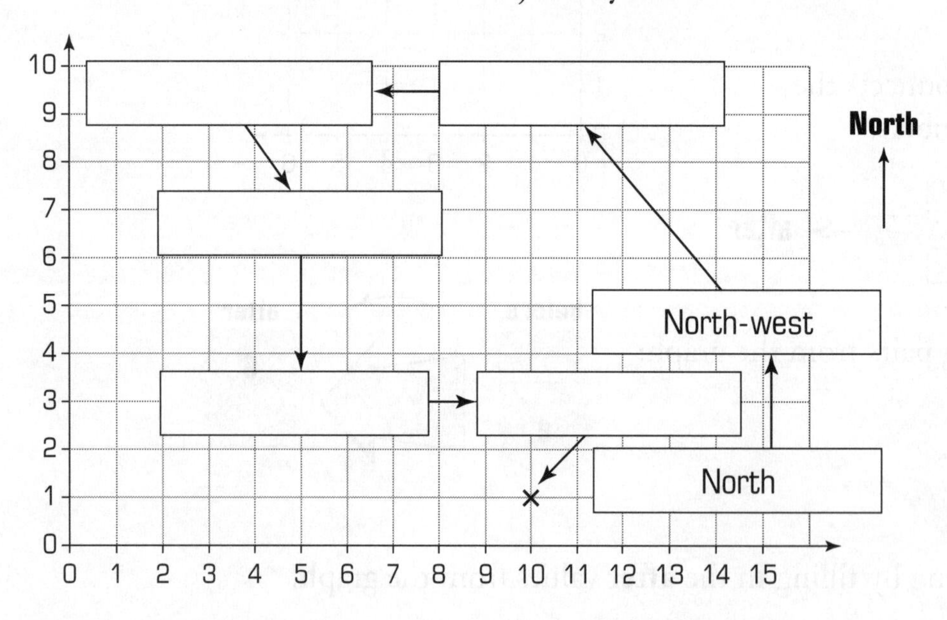

Start at X and follow these coordinates. Which direction are you going in?

b From (**10, 1**) to (**6, 1**) the direction of travel is ________________.

c From (**6, 1**) to (**10, 5**) the direction of travel is ________________.

d From (**10, 5**) to (**7, 8**) the direction of travel is ________________.

e From (**7, 8**) to (**1, 8**) the direction of travel is ________________.

f From (**1, 8**) to (**1, 3**) the direction of travel is ________________.

Drawing angles

1 Draw these angles on this protractor.

a 100° **b** 40° **c** 140°
d 70° **e** 120°

Label each angle. The first has been done for you.

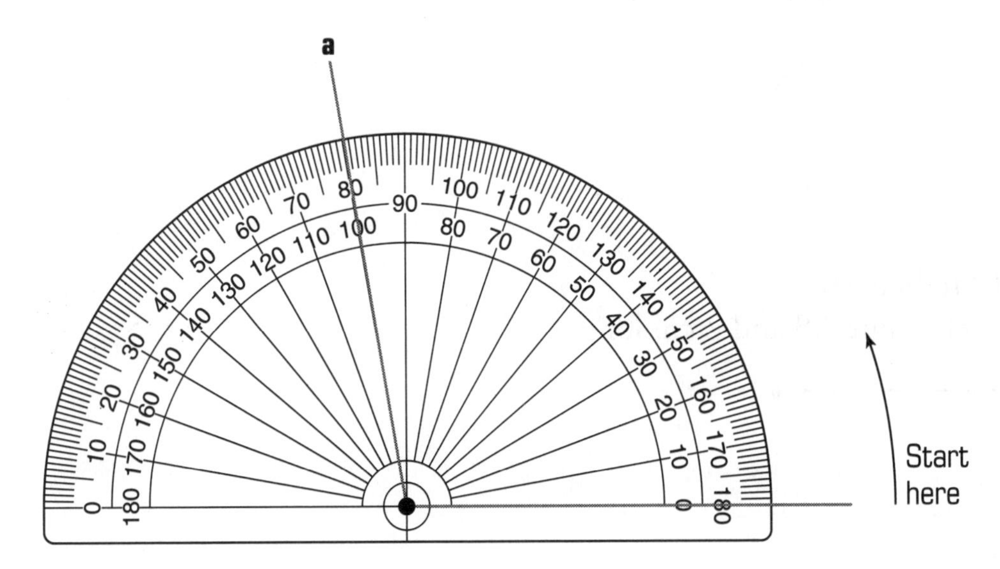

2 Use a protractor to draw these angles.
Place the cross on the dot.

a 50° **b** 80°

c 130° **d** 20°

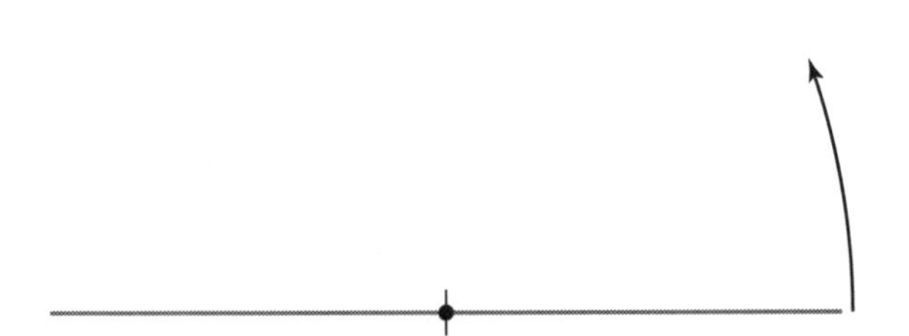

Parallel and perpendicular lines

1 Use a ruler to check if lines A and B are parallel to each other.

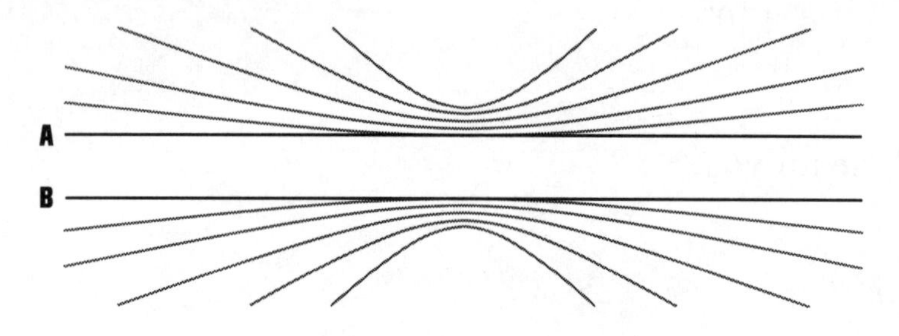

Are the lines parallel? _______

2 Draw a line parallel to line AB.
It should be 2 cm below line AB and 7 cm long.

A ———————————— B

3 Draw a line perpendicular to each of these lines.
A protractor has been drawn for you.

a

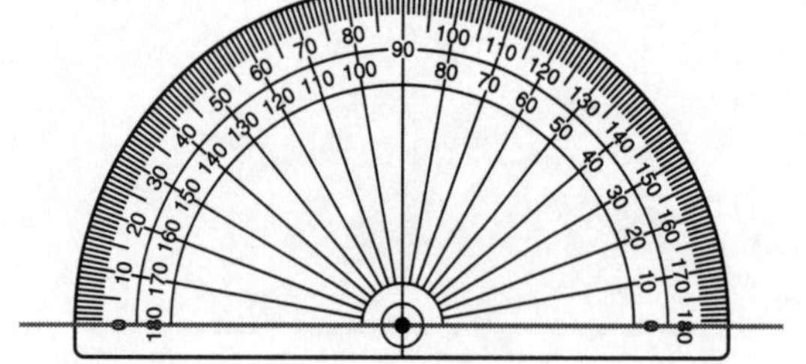

b

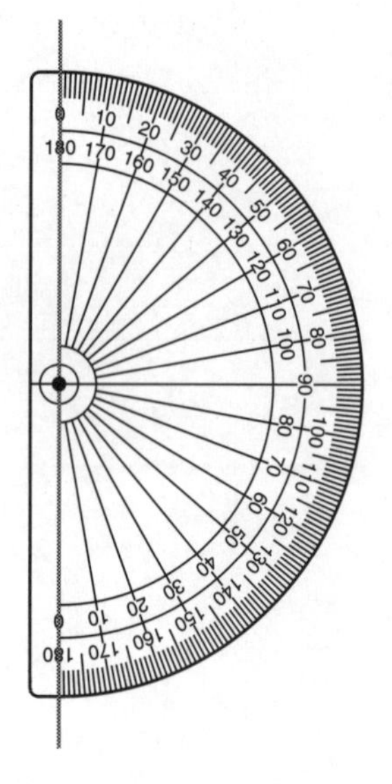

4 Draw a line perpendicular to line GH.

G ———————————— H

N4.1WS Fractions

1 What fraction of each shape is shaded?

a 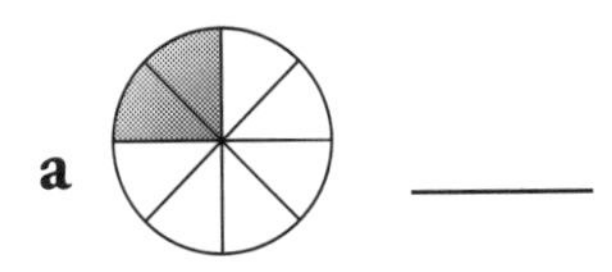 ______

b 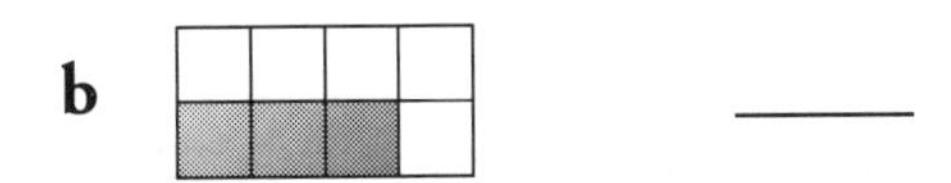 ______

c 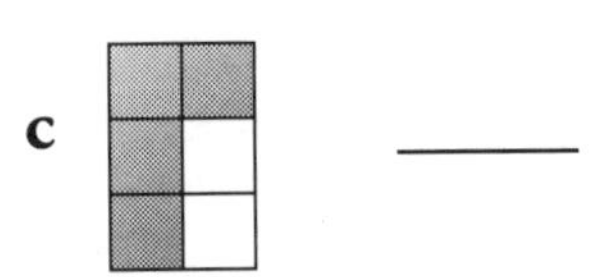 ______

d 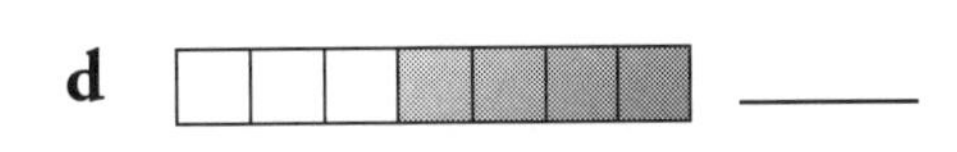 ______

2 Use the shapes to write these as a simpler fraction:

a $\frac{5}{10}$ or ______

b $\frac{3}{9}$ or ______

c $\frac{2}{8}$ or ______

d $\frac{10}{20}$ or ______

e $\frac{3}{12}$ or ______

f $\frac{2}{10}$ or ______

3 To simplify $\frac{6}{10}$ you divide top and bottom by the same number.

$\frac{6}{10} = \frac{3}{5}$ (÷ 2 top, ÷ 2 bottom)

$\frac{6}{10}$ is the same as $\frac{3}{5}$.

Simplify these fractions.

a $\frac{3}{9} = \frac{}{3}$ (÷ 3 top, ÷ 3 bottom)

b $\frac{4}{10} = \frac{}{5}$ (÷ 2 top, ÷ 2 bottom)

c $\frac{4}{12} =$ ___ (÷ 4 top, ÷ 4 bottom)

d $\frac{6}{15} =$ ___ (÷ 3 top, ÷ 3 bottom)

e $\frac{5}{15} =$ ___ (÷ 5 top, ÷ 5 bottom)

f $\frac{6}{16} =$ ___ (÷ 2 top, ÷ 2 bottom)

Fractions and decimals

1 How much of each shape is shaded?
Give your answer as a fraction and a decimal.
The first is done for you.

a

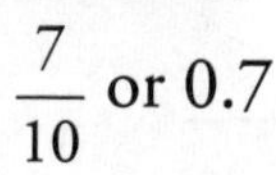

$\frac{7}{10}$ or 0.7

b

_____ or _____

c

_____ or _____

d

_____ or _____

e

_____ or _____

f

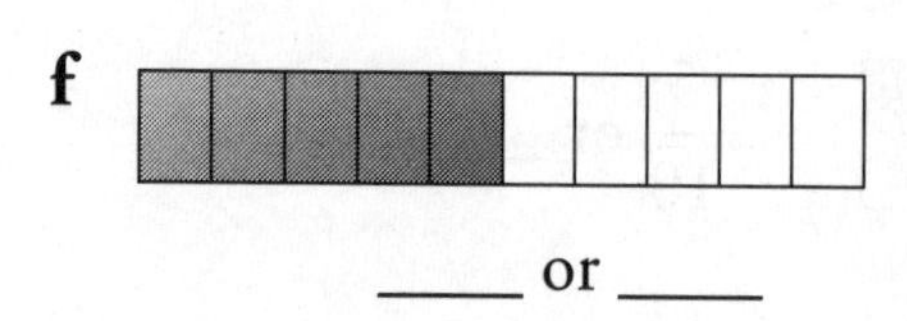

_____ or _____

2 Shade in these parts of this 10 × 10 square.
The first has been done for you.

A $\frac{4}{100}$ or 0.04 **B** $\frac{7}{100}$ or 0.07

C $\frac{5}{100}$ or 0.05 **D** $\frac{10}{100}$ or 0.1

E $\frac{14}{100}$ or 0.14 **F** $\frac{17}{100}$ or 0.17

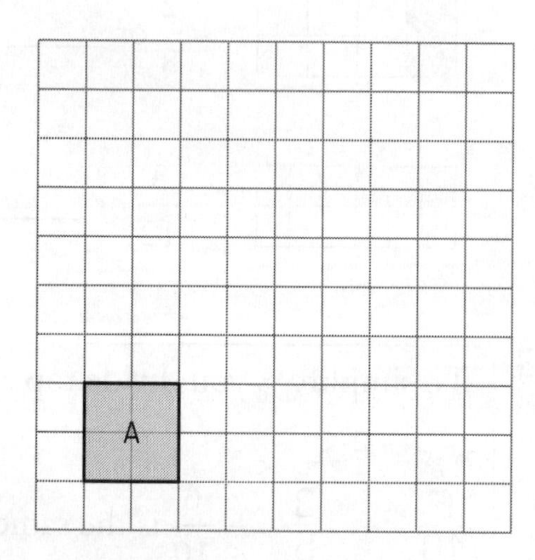

3 Write these fractions as decimals.
The first one is done for you.

a $\frac{6}{100}$ = 0.06 **b** $\frac{10}{100}$ = _______ **c** $\frac{16}{100}$ = _______

d $\frac{25}{100}$ = _______ **e** $\frac{65}{100}$ = _______ **f** $\frac{40}{100}$ = _______

4 Write these decimals as fractions.
The first one is done for you.

a 0.02 = $\frac{2}{100}$ **b** 0.15 = _____ **c** 0.35 = _____

d 0.80 = _____ **e** 0.33 = _____ **f** 0.90 = _____

N4.4WS Percentages of amounts

1 A pizza is cut into 10 equal slices. Each slice is 10% of the whole pizza.

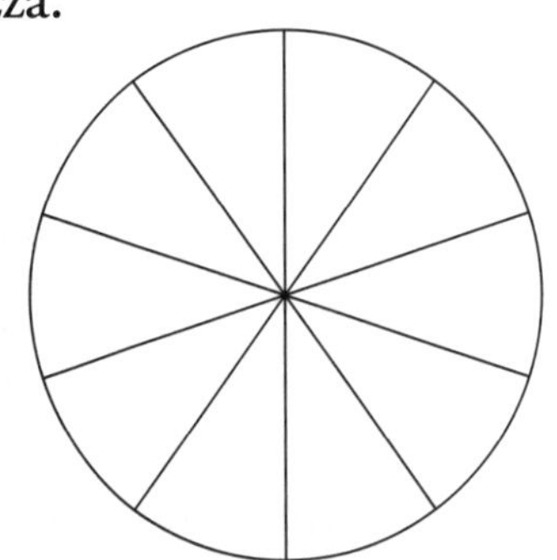

a Colour 3 slices blue. What percentage is this? ________%

b Colour 3 slices green. What percentage is this? ________%

c Colour 3 slices red. What percentage is this? ________%

d What percentage of the pizza is left? ________%

e What percentage is **half** a slice of pizza? ________%

2 Here are 20 counters: 

Share them equally into the percentage strip.

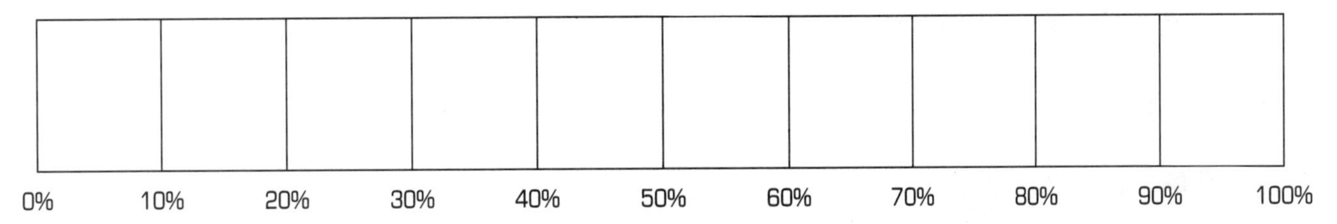

Use the strip to work out:

a 50% of 20 counters = ______

b 10% of 20 counters = ______

c 30% of 20 counters = ______

d 80% of 20 counters = ______

3 Here are 50 counters:

Share them equally into the percentage strip.

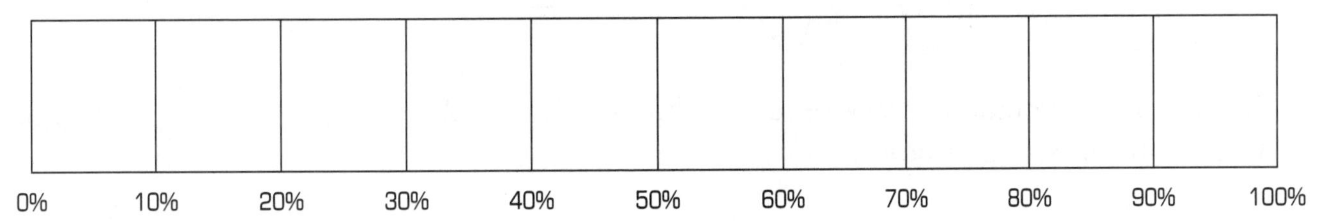

Use the strip to work out:

a 10% of 50 counters = ______

b 30% of 50 counters = ______

c 50% of 50 counters = ______

d 80% of 50 counters = ______

N4.5WS Ratio

1 **a** Colour 4 of these tins red and 3 tins blue.

b What is the ratio of red to blue? ___ : ___

2 **a** Colour 3 of these tins red and 6 tins blue.

b What is the ratio of red to blue? ___ : ___

3 What is the ratio of black beads to white beads on these strings?

a ______ : ______

b ______ : ______

c ______ : ______

d ______ : ______

4 This string of beads is made up from black and white beads in the ratio of 1 : 4.
Colour in the string of beads.

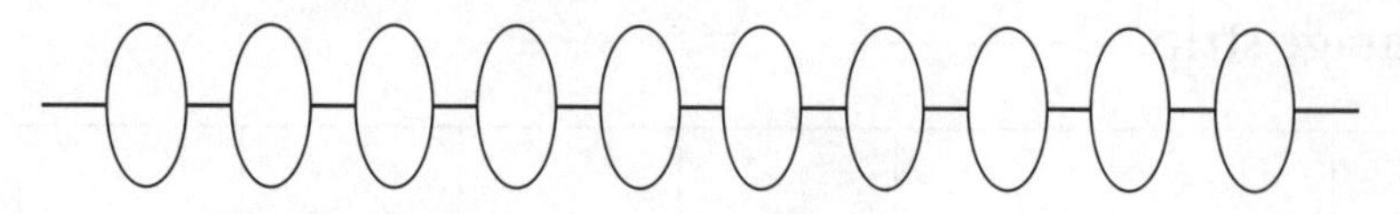

5 In this string the ratio of black beads to white beads is 3 : 2.
Colour in this string of beads.

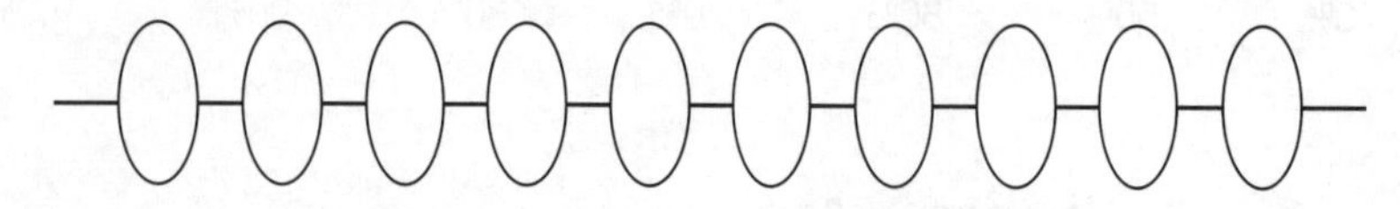

6 The ratio of black beads to white beads on a string is 2 : 1.
There are 10 black beads.

How many white beads are needed? ___________

Equalities

1 Write numbers in the boxes to make the answer 20.

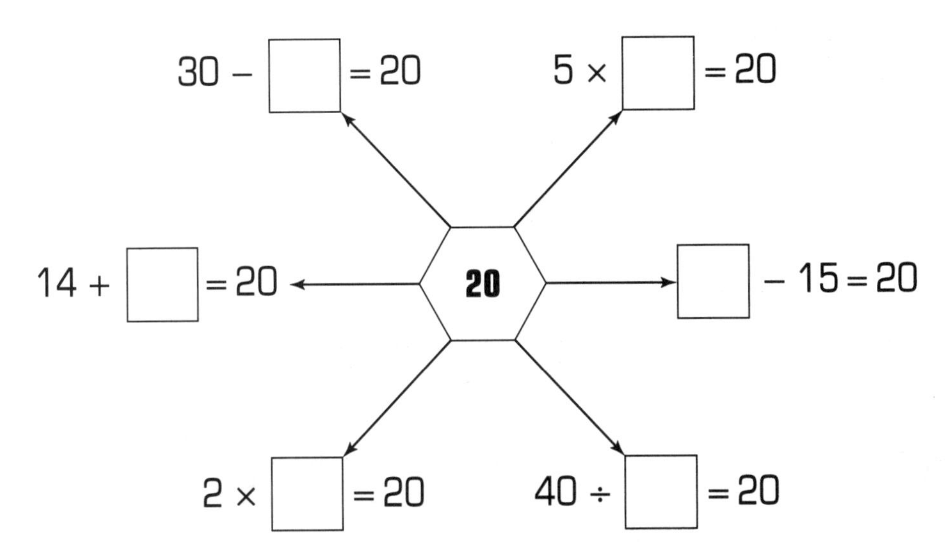

2 Continue these strips to the given length.

a **9 cm** 4 cm

How long is the new piece? _______ cm

b **10 cm**

How long is the new piece? _______ cm

c **13 cm**

How long is the new piece? _______ cm

3 **a** Measure these lines. A = _______ B = _______ C = _______ D = _______

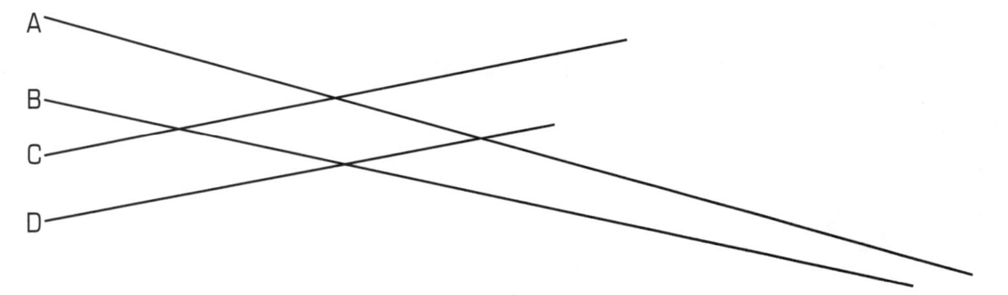

b There are two pairs of lines. Each pair add up to 20 cm.
Find the two pairs.

Pair 1 (_____ and _____)

Pair 2 (_____ and _____)

A4.4WS Equations

1 Calculate the weights of the parcels needed to make the scales balance.
Write the weights onto the parcels.

a

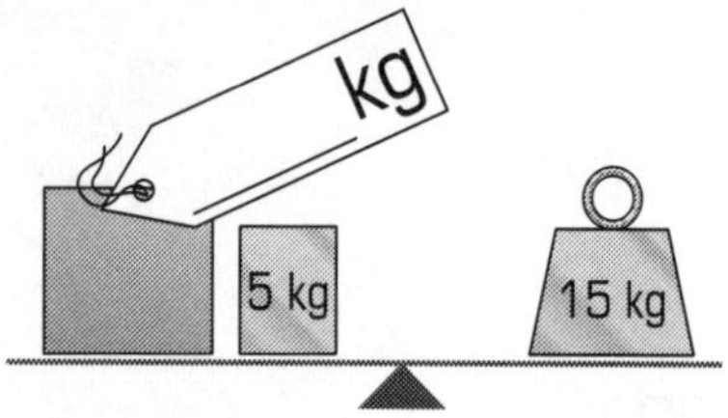

b

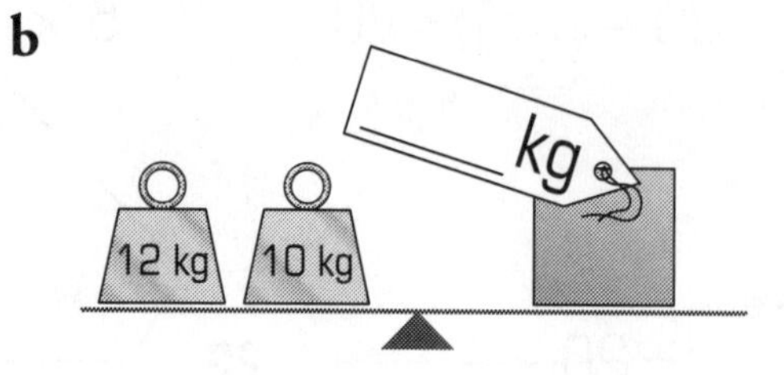

c

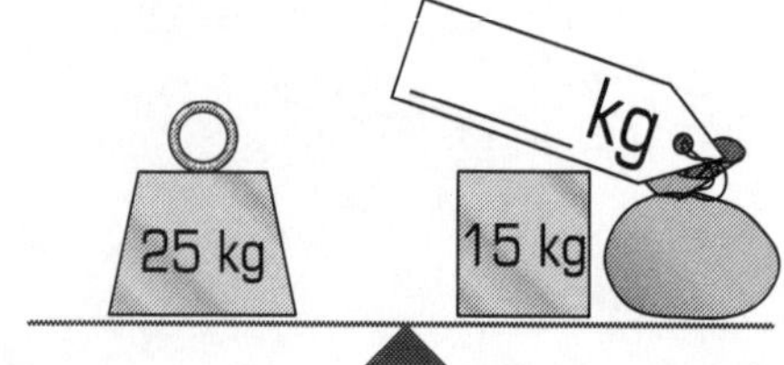

d

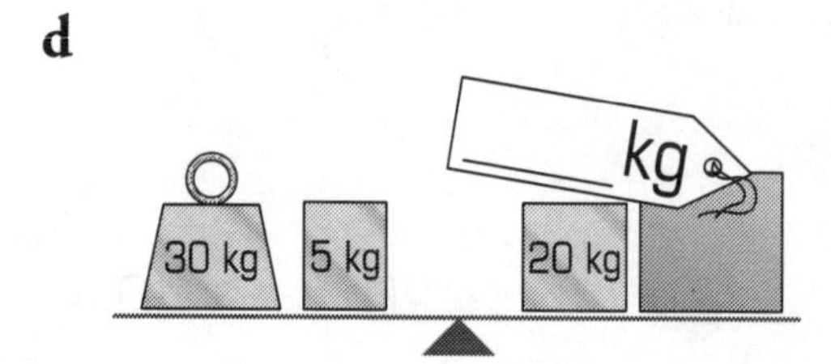

e

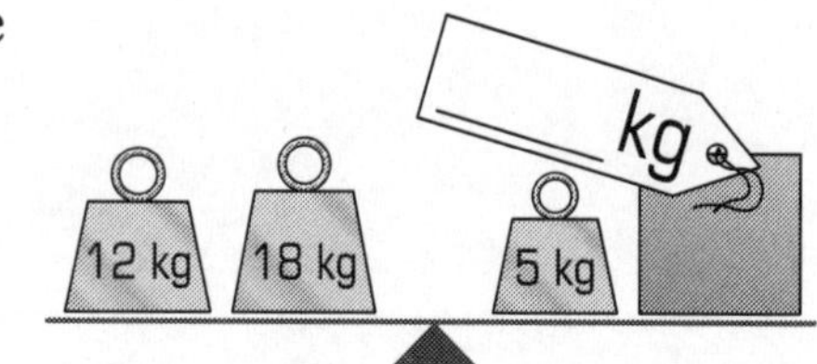

f

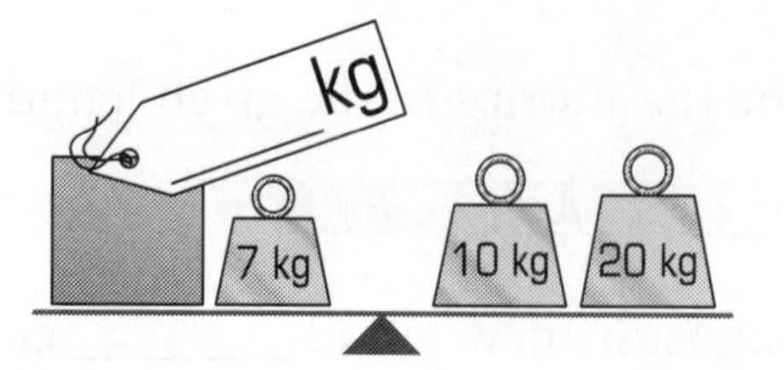

2 Write weights onto this drawing to make these scales balance.

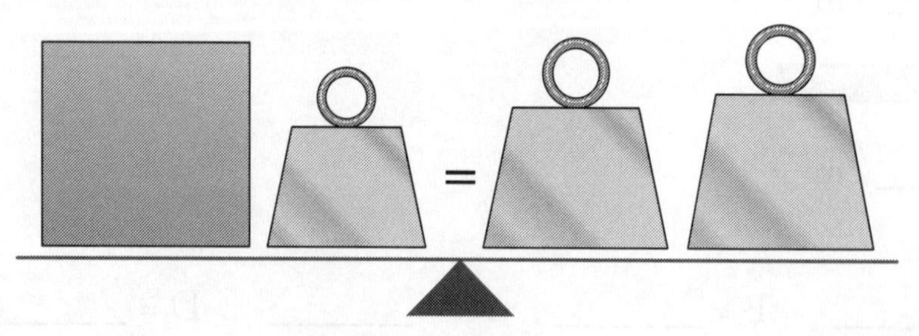

3 Write weights onto these parcels to make the scales **unbalanced**.

a

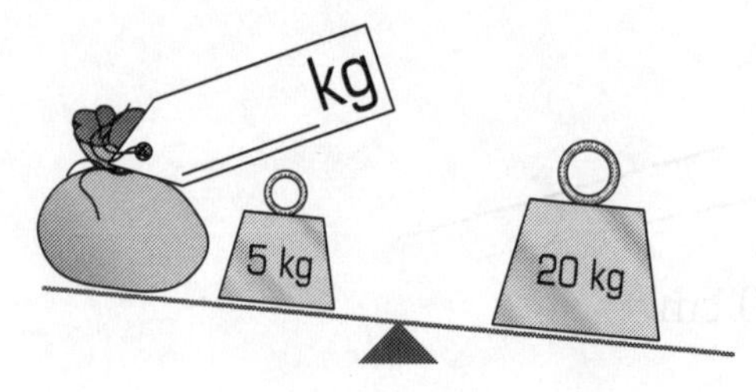

b

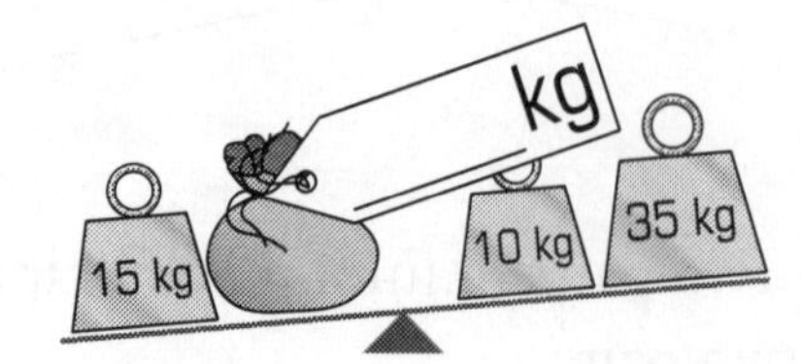

S4.1WS Symmetry

Draw all the lines of symmetry onto these shapes.
Remember to use a ruler.

The lines of symmetry are dashed lines.

1

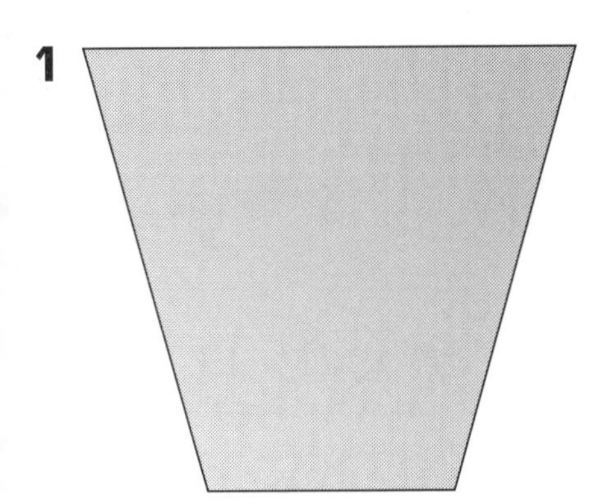

2

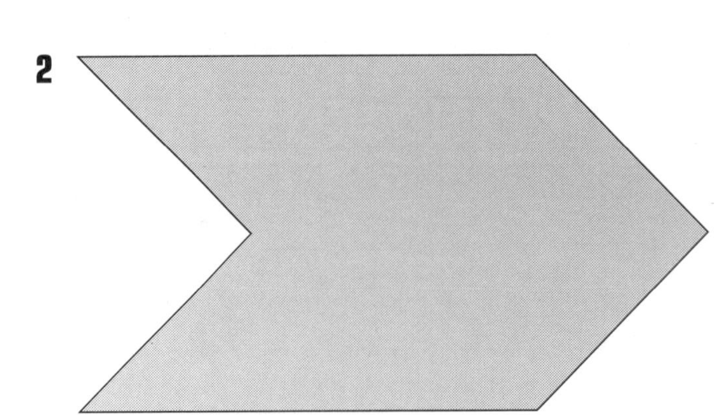

3

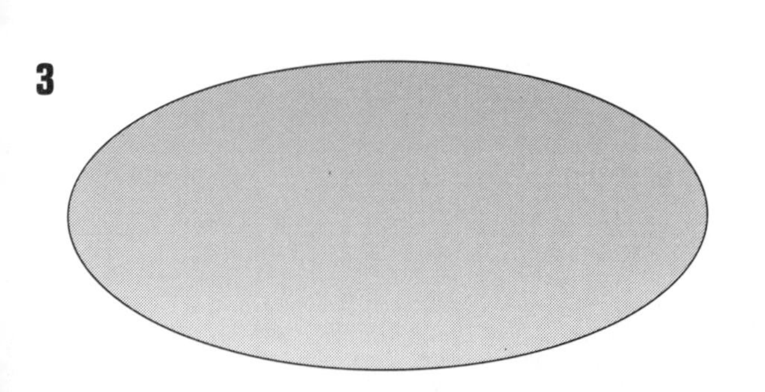

4

5

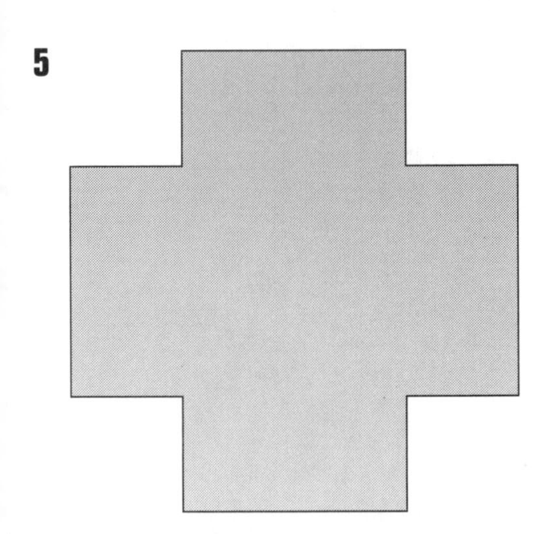

6

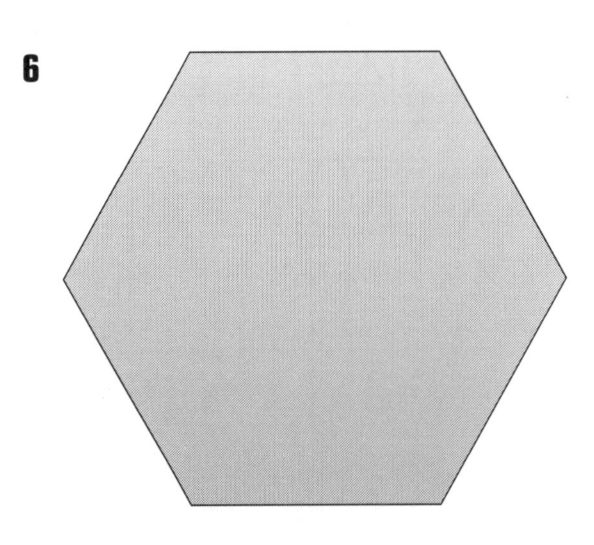

S4.2WS Reflection symmetry

1 Draw the reflection of each shape in the mirror line.

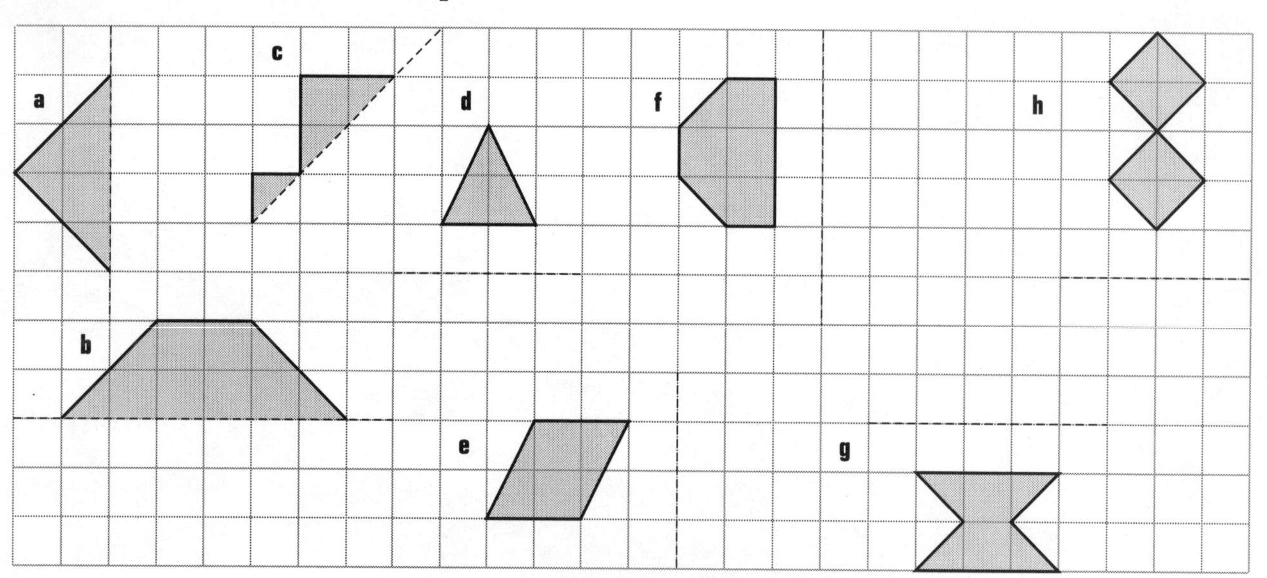

2 Reflect this drawing in the mirror line to complete the 'happy' face.

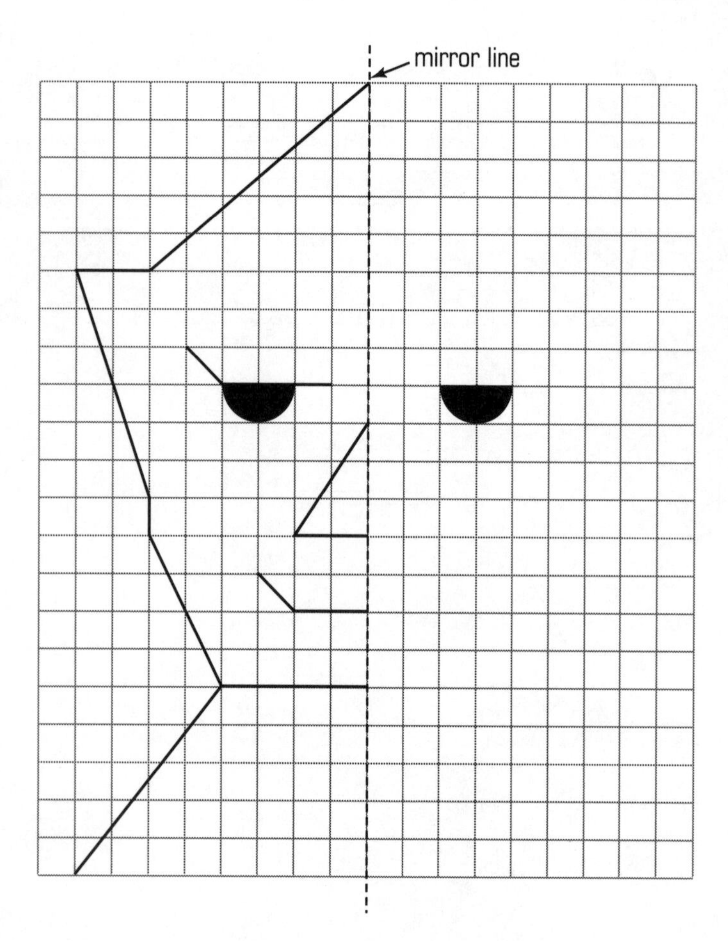

S4.4WS Translating shapes

1 Use these instructions to translate each shape and draw its new position. The first one is done for you

Shape **a**	8 right and 3 up
Shape **b**	10 right and 2 down
Shape **c**	7 left and 2 down
Shape **d**	5 left and 3 up
Shape **e**	2 left and 4 up

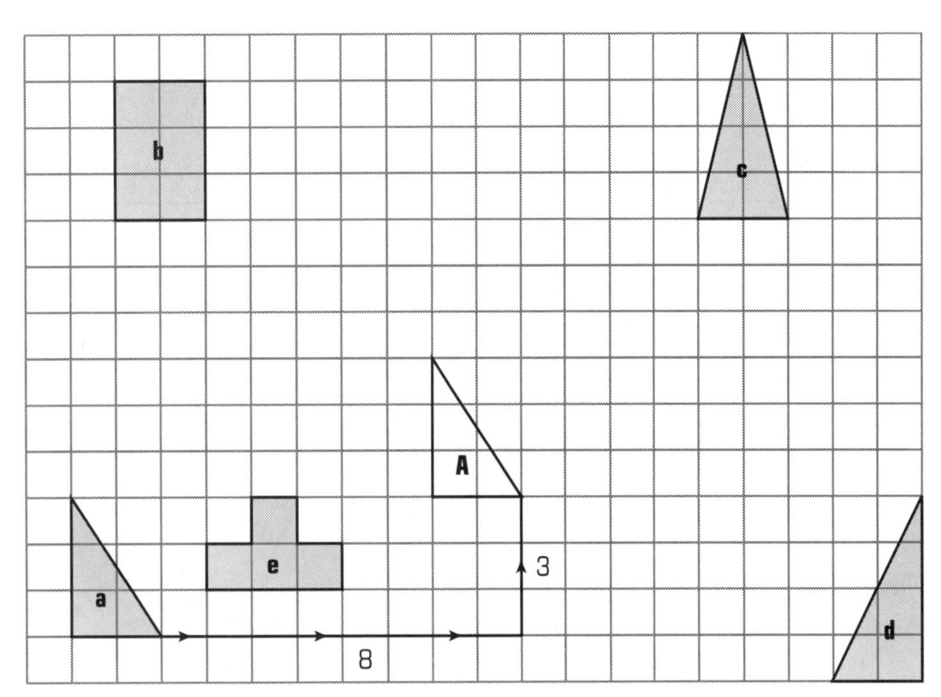

2 Describe the translation of each shape.

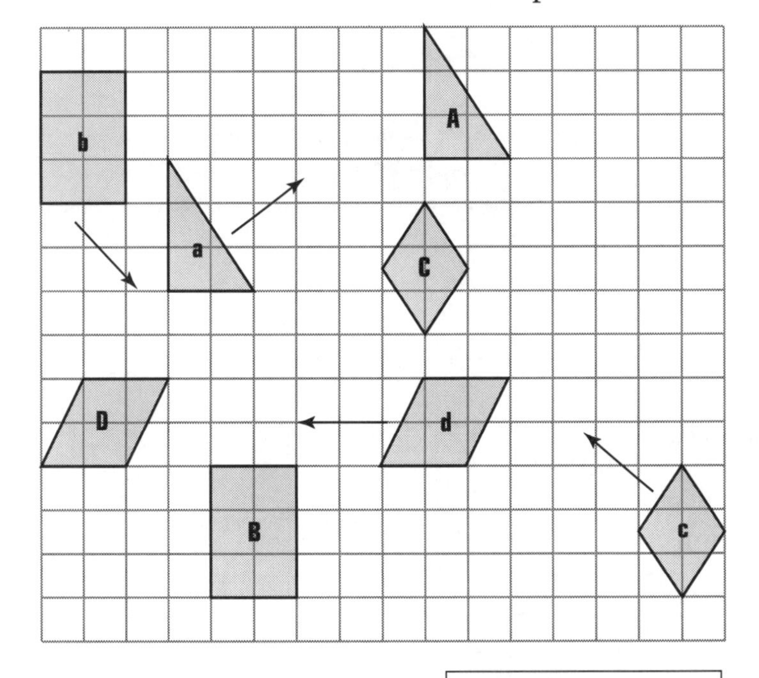

Count across first then up or down

a to **A** 6 right and

_____ up

b to **B** ____ right and

_____ down

c to **C** ______________________

____

d to **D** ______________________

____

1 How many degrees are shown in these angles?

a

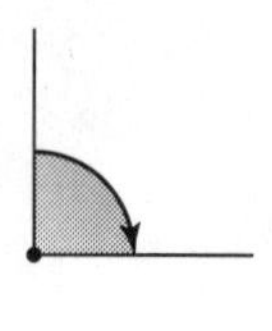

______°

b

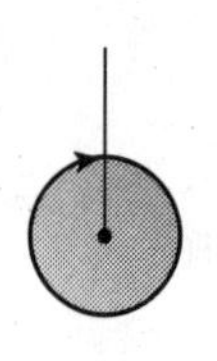

______°

c

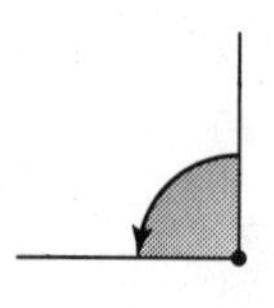

______°

d

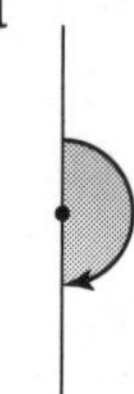

______°

2 One wheel is turning clockwise and the other is turning anti-clockwise.
Label each wheel correctly.

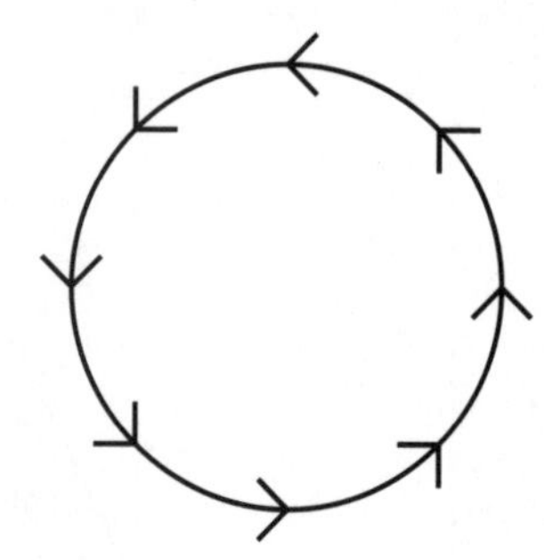

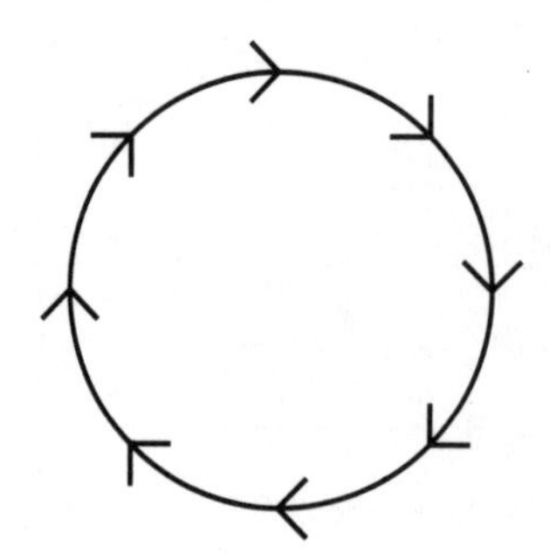

______________ ______________

3 Rotate this shape through 180°.
Draw the new shape.

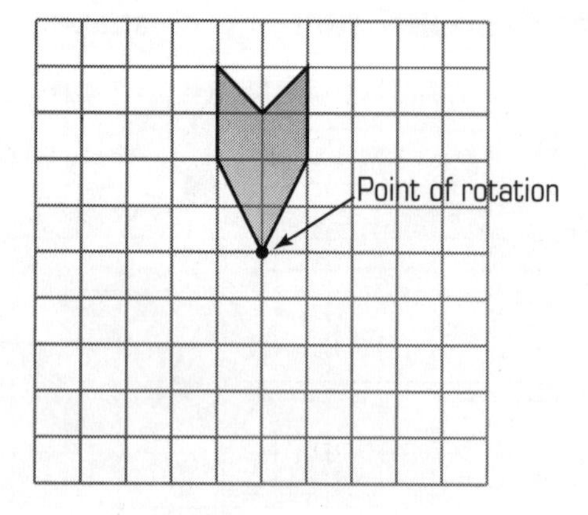

4 **a** Rotate this shape **A** through 90° clockwise.
Label the new shape **B**.

b Now, rotate the original shape **A** through 90° anti-clockwise.
Label the new shape **C**.

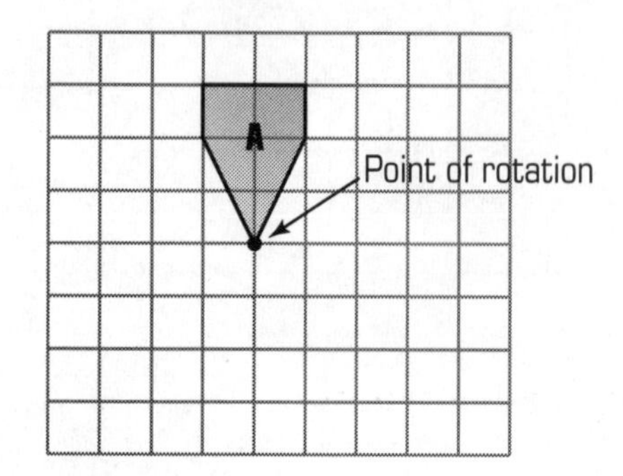

N5.1WS Estimating

1 Estimate each of these measures.
Write the units that you are using to estimate each measure.

Item	Estimate	Units
Length of your classroom		(m) metres
Height of the classroom door		
Height of your friend		
Weight of your Framework book		
How many students in your school		students
Cost of a portion of fish and chips		
Weight of a cricket ball		
Flight time from London to New York		
The length of a marathon race	42	
The cost to run your school for one year		

2 The distance from London to Edinburgh is about 600 km.
Estimate the distance in km between these towns.

a London to Cambridge

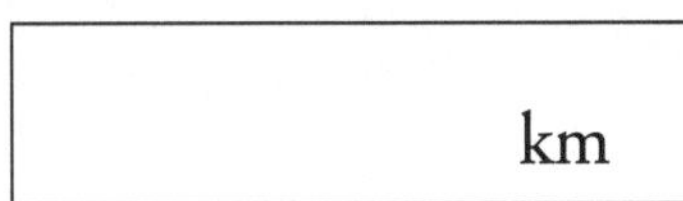

b Brighton to London

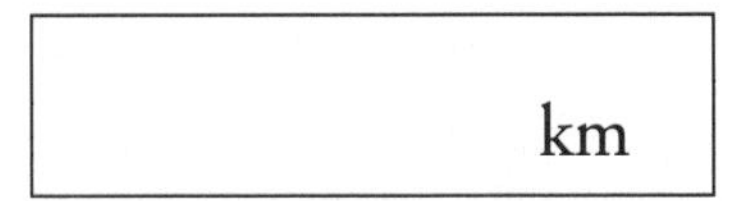

c Cardiff to Cambridge

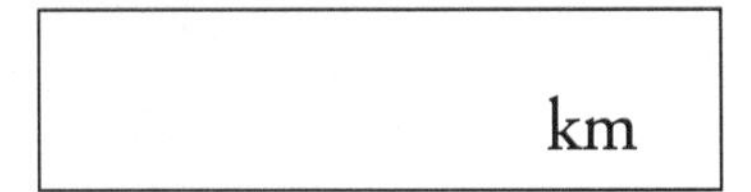

d Edinburgh to Weymouth

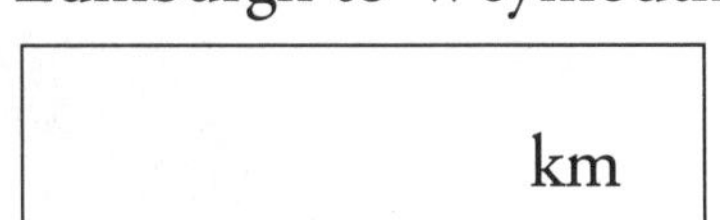

Using factors

1 Rearrange these squares to make as many different rectangles as you can.
Draw on the grids to help you.

a

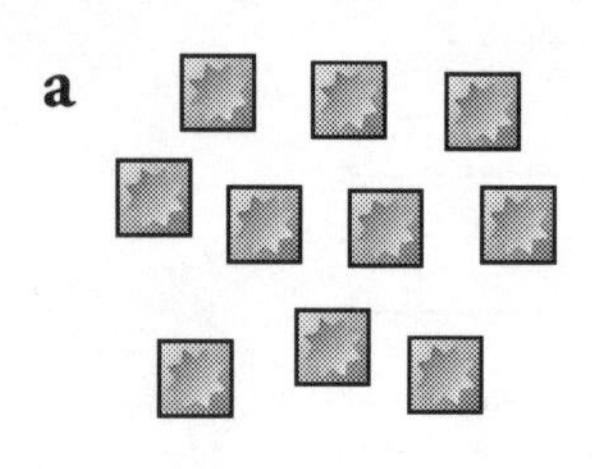

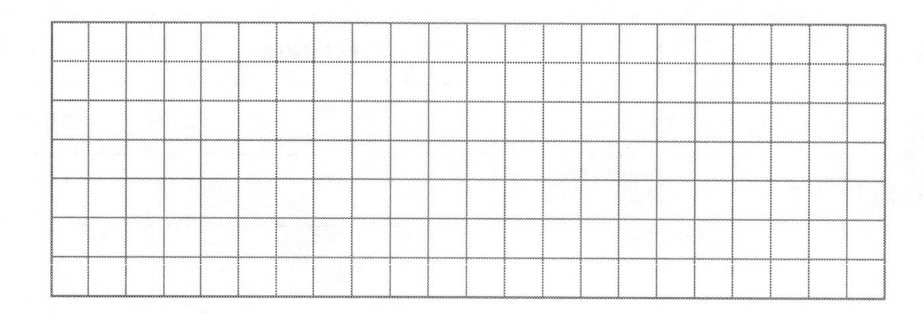

What are the **factor pairs** of 10? ______________________

b

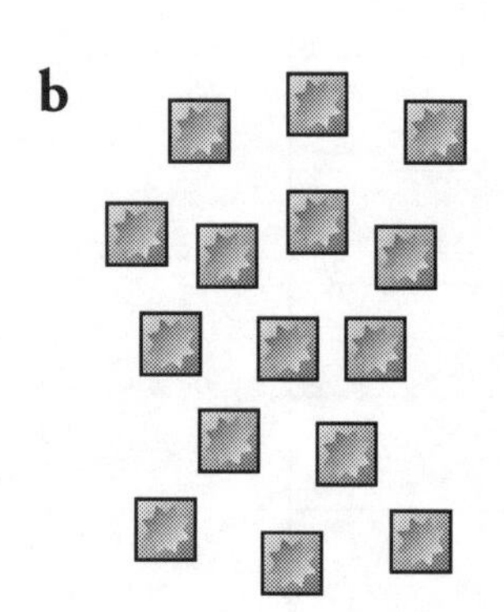

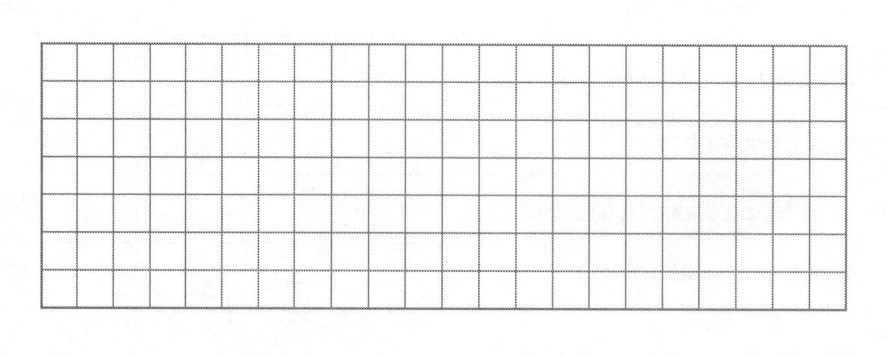

What are the **factor pairs** of 15? ______________________

2 Fill in this table to complete these calculations.

Multiplication	Factors	First multiplication	Second multiplication	Third multiplication
(17) × 4	4 = 2 × 2	(17) × 2 = (34)	34 × 2 = ☐	
15 × 8	8 = 2 × 2 × 2	15 × 2 = ☐	30 × 2 = ☐	60 × 2 = ☐
12 × 6	6 = 2 × 3	12 × 2 = ☐	24 × 3 = ☐	
21 × 9	9 = ☐ × ☐	21 × 3 = ☐	63 × 3 = ☐	
15 × 6	6 = ☐ × ☐	15 × 2 = ☐	30 × 3 = ☐	
14 × 12	12 = 2 × 2 × 3	14 × 2 = ☐	☐ × 2 = ☐	56 × 3 = ☐
25 × 10	10 = 2 × 5	25 × 2 = ☐	☐ × 5 = ☐	

N5.4WS Written calculations

1 Split up these numbers into hundreds, tens and units.
For example: 163 = 100 + 60 + 3

a 175 = __________ + __________ + __________

b 98 = __________ + __________

c 209 = __________ + __________

d 530 = __________ + __________

2 Use these grids to complete these multiplications.

a 32 × 3 = __________

×	30	2
3		

b 43 × 4 = __________

×	40	3
4		

c 65 × 6 = __________

×	60	5
6		

d 28 × 7 = __________

×	20	8
7		

e 92 × 4 = __________

×		

f 54 × 7 = __________

×		

g 124 × 3 = __________

×	100	20	4
3			

h 136 × 3 = __________

×			

Fill in the spaces to help you complete the divisions.

1 $93 \div 3$

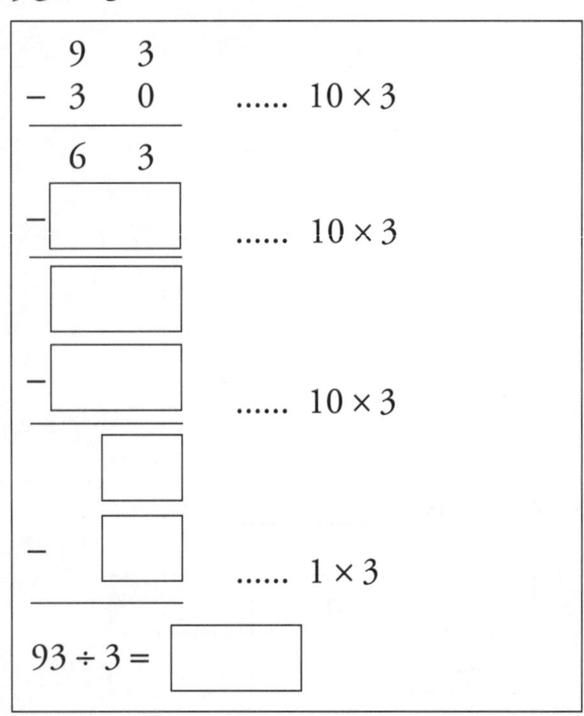

2 $192 \div 6$

1 9 2
− 6 0 ….. 10 × 6
1 3 2
− …… 10 × 6
− …… ×
− …… ×

192 ÷ 6 =

3 $108 \div 9$

1 0 8
− 9 0 ….. × 9
− …… × 9

108 ÷ 9 =

4 $92 \div 4$

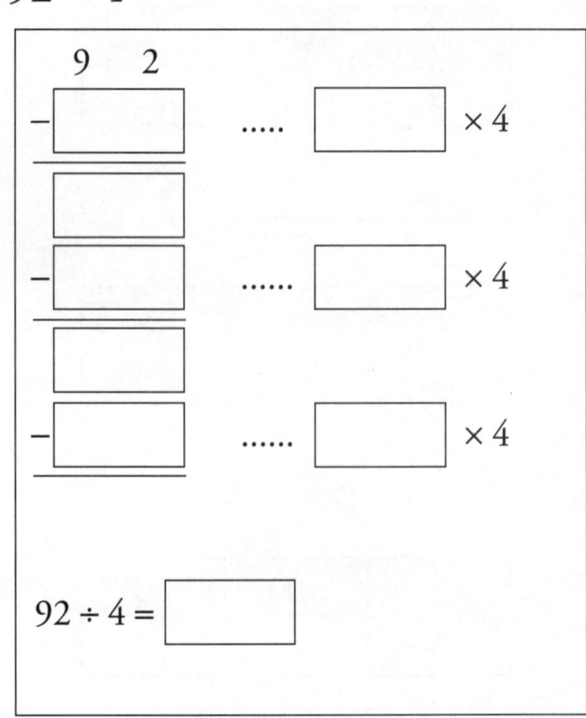

Equivalent fractions

1 ▶ Shade $\frac{1}{2}$ of each shape.

▶ Write the fraction that is equivalent to $\frac{1}{2}$ in each drawing.

a

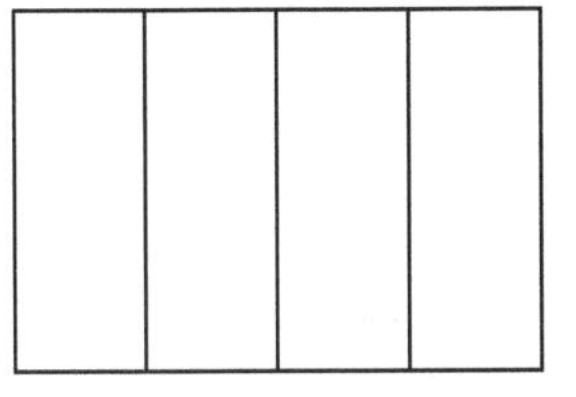

$\frac{1}{2}$ is the same as

b

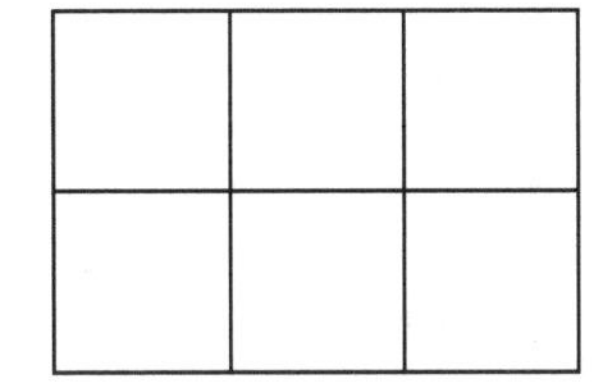

$\frac{1}{2}$ is the same as

c

$\frac{1}{2}$ is the same as

d

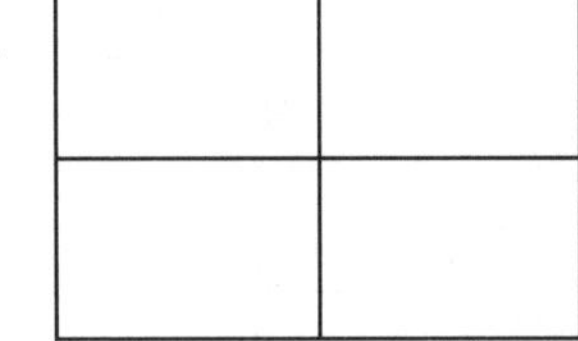

$\frac{1}{2}$ is the same as

2 Shade $\frac{1}{5}$ of this shape.

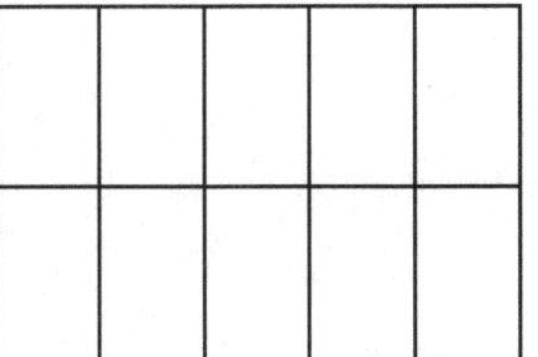

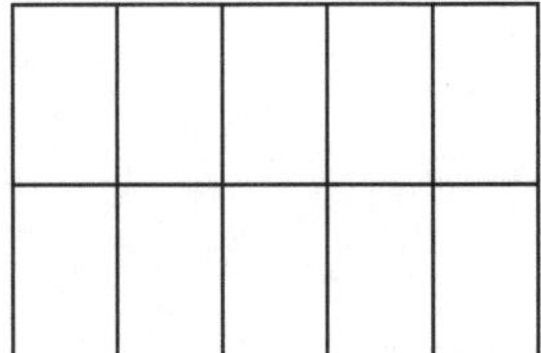

$\frac{1}{5}$ is the same as

3 Shade $\frac{1}{4}$ of this shape.

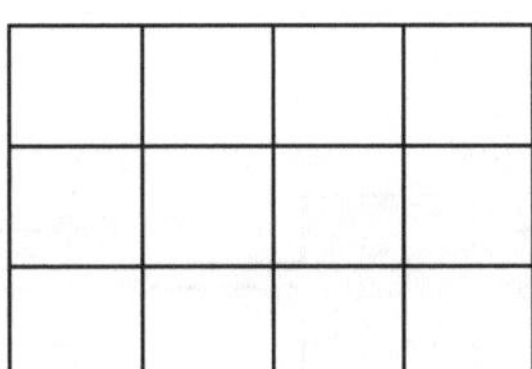

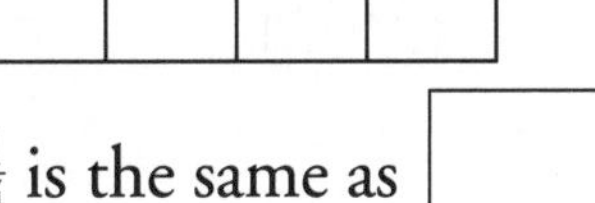

$\frac{1}{4}$ is the same as

4 Shade $\frac{1}{6}$ of this shape.

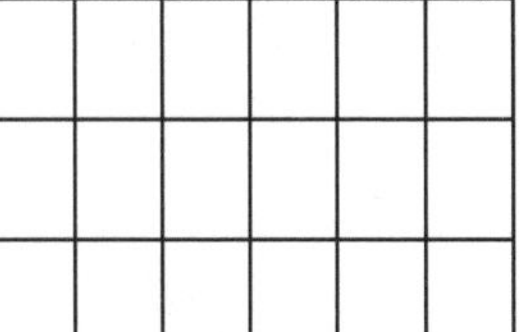

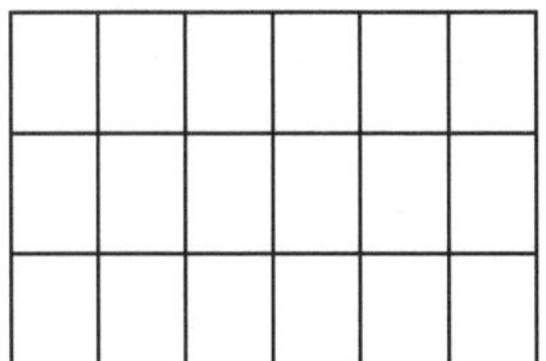

$\frac{1}{6}$ is the same as

5 Shade $\frac{1}{5}$ of this shape.

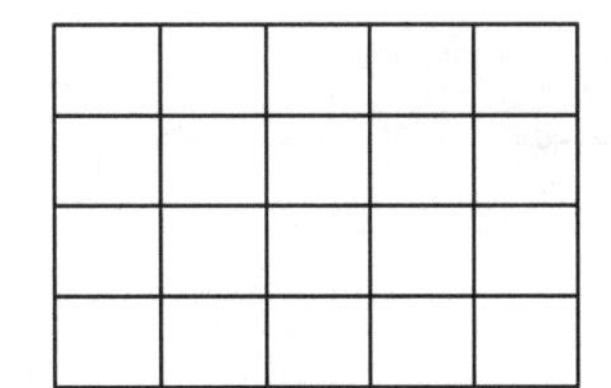

$\frac{1}{5}$ is the same as

N5.7WS Finding fractions of amounts

1 Which division goes with each calculation?
Draw arrows to connect them.

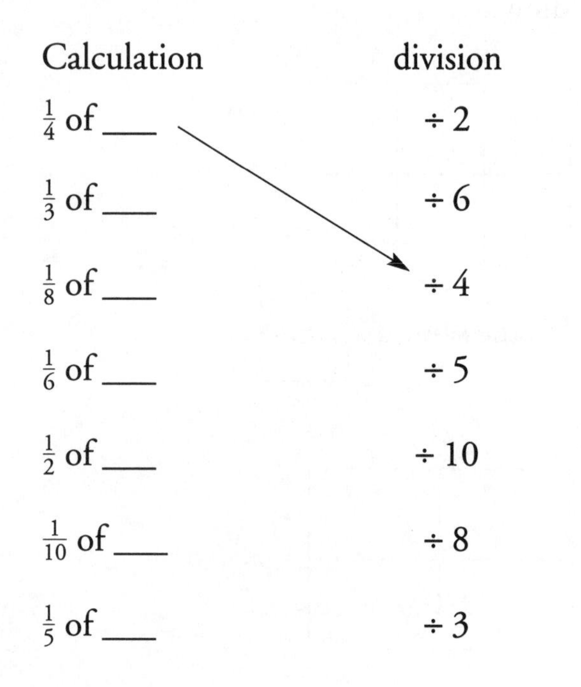

For example:
$\frac{1}{4}$ of 12 means $12 \div 4 = 3$

2 Use the machines to find these fractions of amounts.

a $\frac{3}{4}$ of 12: 12 → ÷ 4 → ☐ → × 3 → = ☐

b $\frac{3}{4}$ of 20: 20 → ÷ 4 → ☐ → × 3 → = ☐

c $\frac{2}{3}$ of 15: 15 → ÷ 3 → ☐ → × 2 → = ☐

d $\frac{2}{3}$ of 30: 30 → ÷ 3 → ☐ → × 2 → = ☐

e $\frac{4}{5}$ of 25: 25 → ÷ ___ → ☐ → × ___ → = ☐

Drawing charts and graphs

1 Use the data to fill in this barchart.

Fruit	Apple	Banana	Pear	Orange
Frequency	4	8	2	6

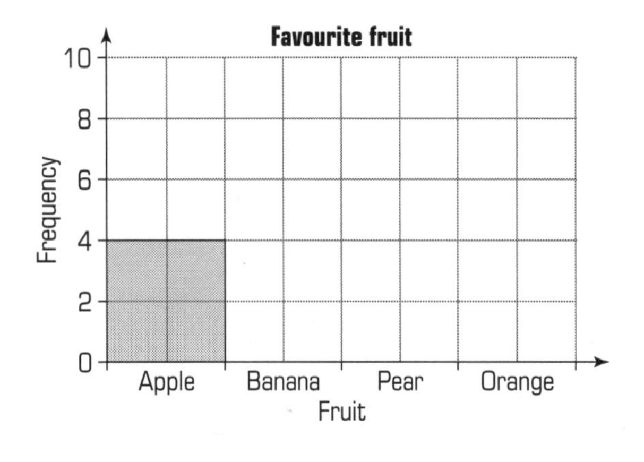

2 Use the data to complete this bar-line graph.

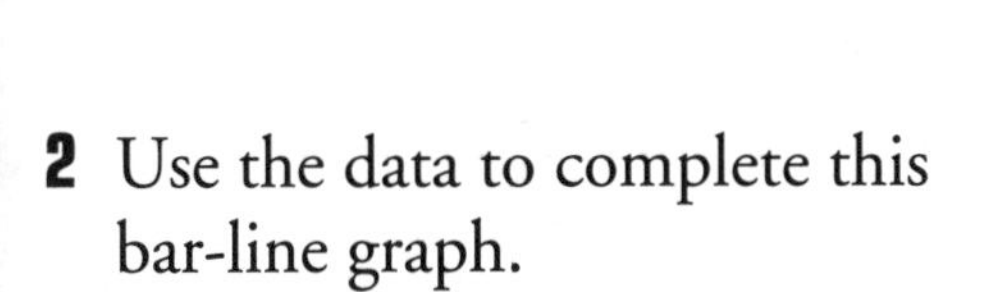

Number of pets	0	1	2	3	4
Frequency	14	10	4	6	2

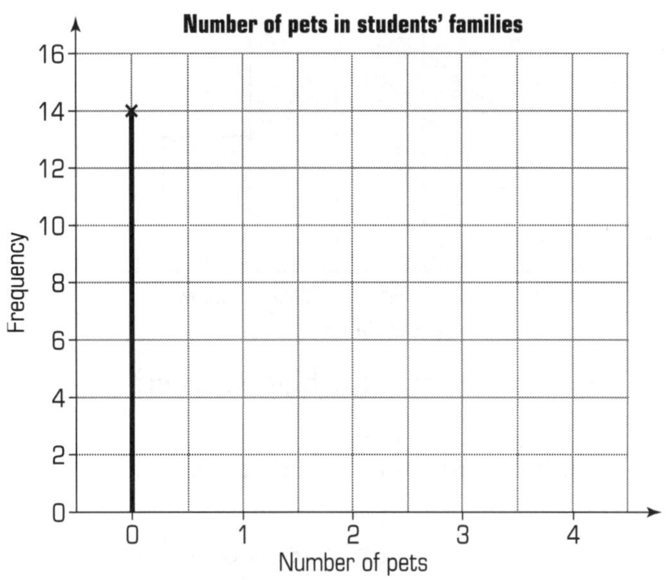

3 Use the data to draw a bar chart.

Bird	Number in garden
Jay	5
Robin	5
Bluetit	10
Crow	20
Sparrow	15

Using statistics

1 This bar chart shows the sale of cars during one week.
The cars are sorted by colour.

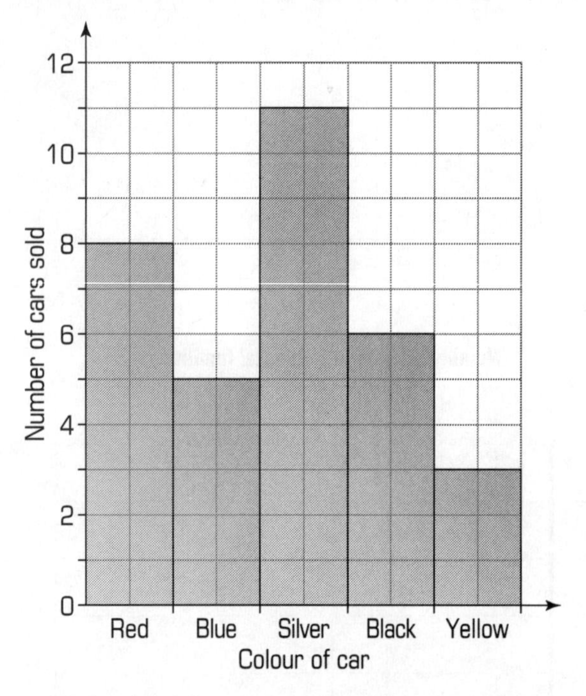

a Which colour was the biggest seller? ____________ This is the mode.

b Which colour was the least popular? ____________

c 5 cars of one colour were sold. What colour were they? ____________

d How many cars were sold in total? ____________________________

2 Draw the data from the bar chart onto this pictogram.
Use the key to help you.

	Number of cars sold
Red	
Blue	
Silver	
Black	
Yellow	

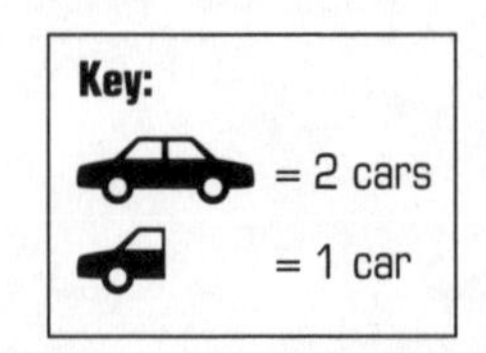

D4.1WS Describing probabilities

1 When this arrow is spun round it can land on white or grey.

a Circle the word that best describes the chance of the spinner landing on grey:

Impossible Unlikely Likely Certain

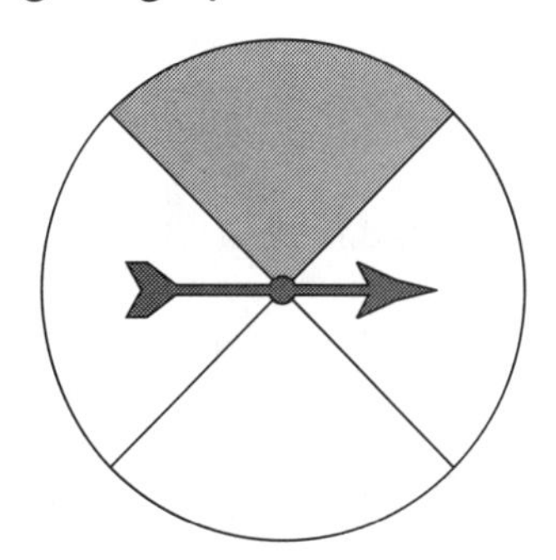

b Describe the chance by putting an X on this probability scale.

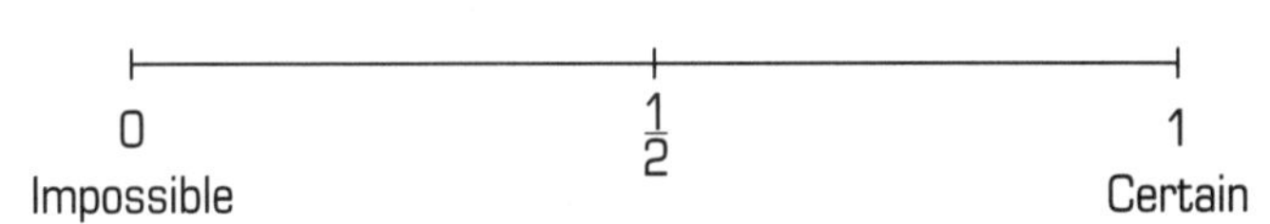

2 Here is another spinner.

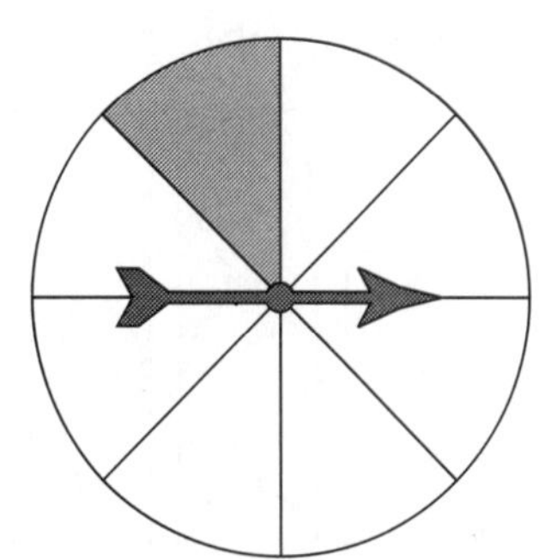

a Complete these statements:

There are ______ possible outcomes.

______ of the outcomes is grey.

There is a ______ in ______ chance of landing on grey.

The probability of landing on grey is ______.

b Describe the probability by putting an X on this probability scale.

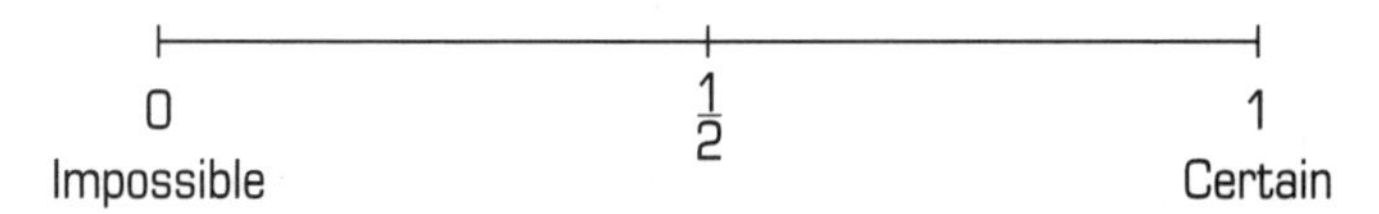

3 As a fraction, write the probability of the arrow landing on grey for each spinner.

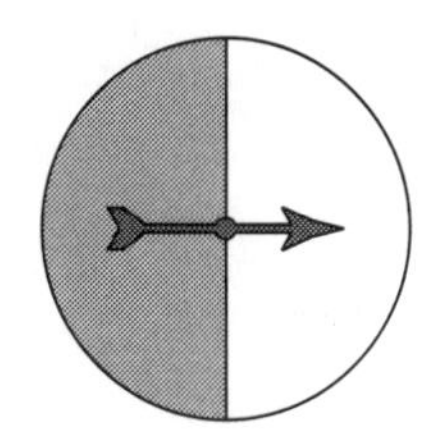
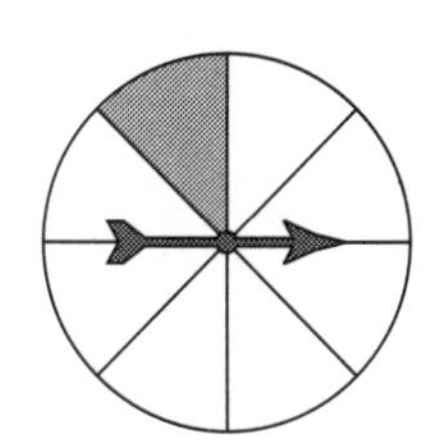
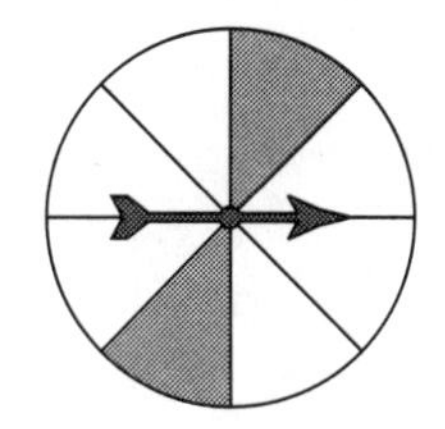
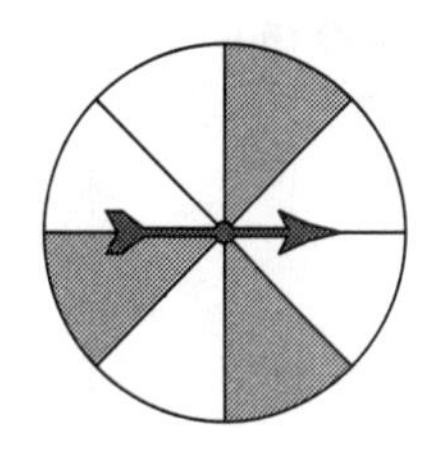
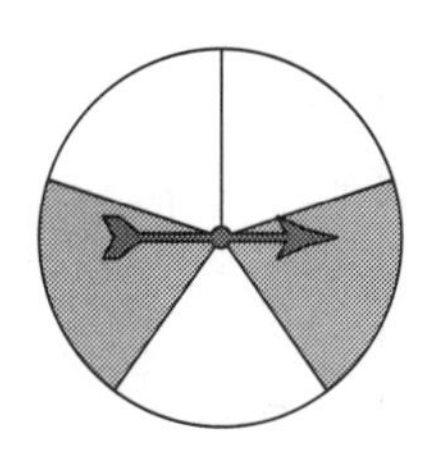

a ________ **b** ________ **c** ________ **d** ________ **e** ________

f Which spinner has the best chance of landing on grey? ________

g Which spinner has the worst chance of landing on grey? ________

D4.2WS A probability experiment

1 If you spin two coins, there are four possible outcomes.

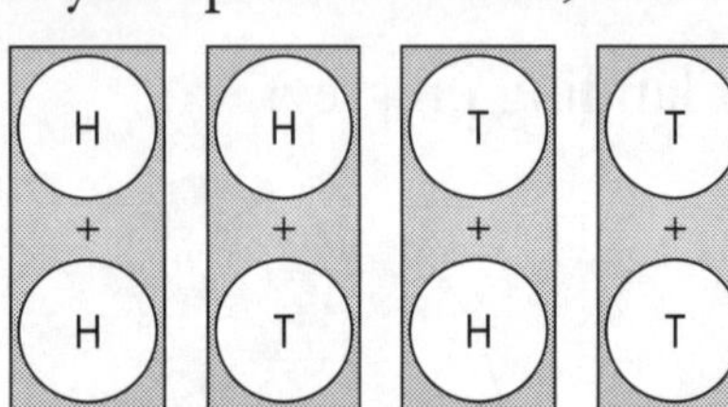

H means heads
T means tails

What are your chances of correctly guessing the outcome?

Answer: ___________ chance in ___________.

2 Fill in as many possible outcomes as you can think of, when you spin three coins. One possible outcome is done for you.

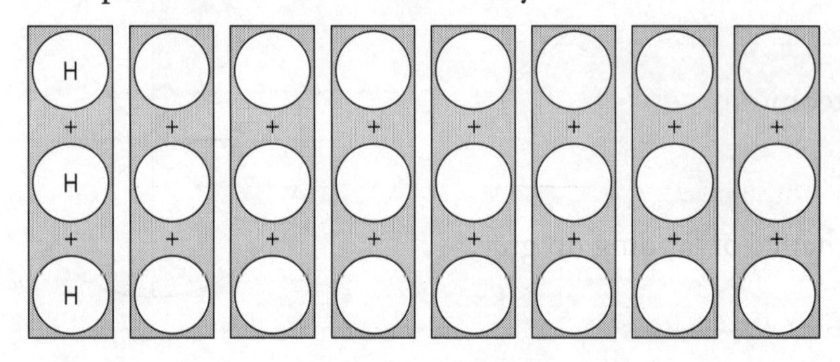

3 Which outcome do you think is the most likely when you spin three coins?

My prediction:

4 Spin three coins 25 times. Record the outcomes on the table as a tally.

Three heads	Two heads and one tail	Two tails and one head	Three tails

5 Which outcome was the most common?

6 Which outcome was the least common?

D4.3WS More experiments

If you roll two dice,

the smallest score you can get is 2 ⇨ ⚀ + ⚀

..... and the biggest score you can get is 12. ⇨ ⚅ + ⚅

1 Roll two dice, 50 times.
Record the scores on this tally chart.

Score	Total	Tally	Frequency
⚀ ⚀	2		
⚀ ⚁	3		
⚁ ⚁ or ⚀ ⚂	4		
⚁ ⚂ or ⚃ ⚀	5		
⚂ ⚂ or ⚃ ⚁	6		
⚃ ⚂ or ⚄ ⚁ or ⚅ ⚀	7		
⚃ ⚃ or ⚅ ⚁ or ⚄ ⚂	8		
⚄ ⚃ or ⚅ ⚂	9		
⚄ ⚄ or ⚅ ⚃	10		
⚅ ⚄	11		
⚅ ⚅	12		

2 Draw your results onto the bar chart.

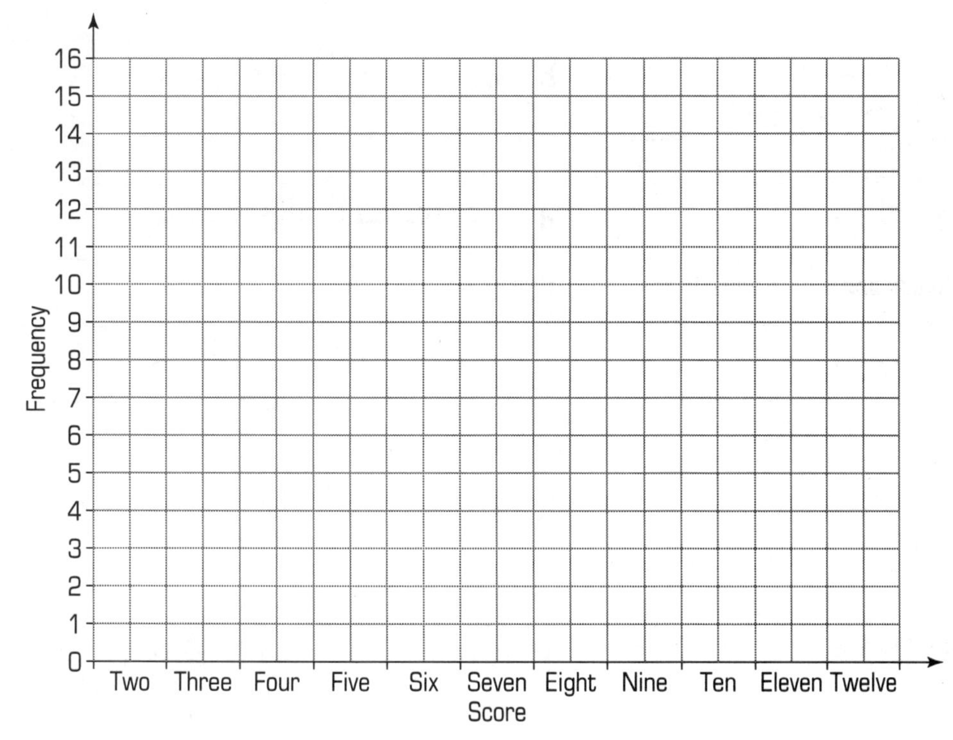

The modal score is the one that occurs most often.

3 What is the modal score? ___________

Using formulas

1 Mike is paid £30 for every car that he makes.
You can show the formula like this:

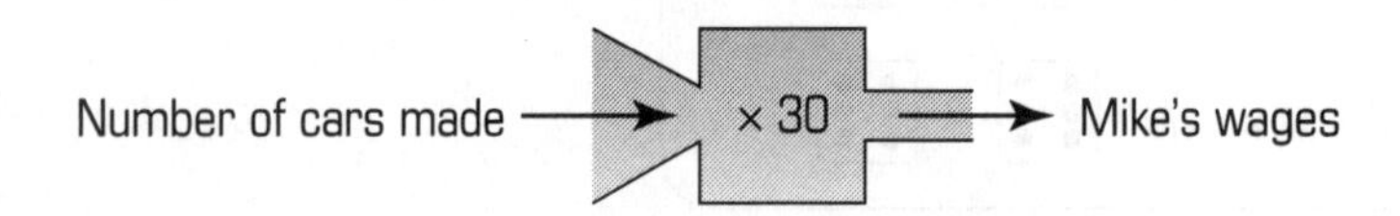

Use the machines to work out Mike's wages for these number of cars made.

To multiply by 30 you multiply by 3 and then multiply by 10

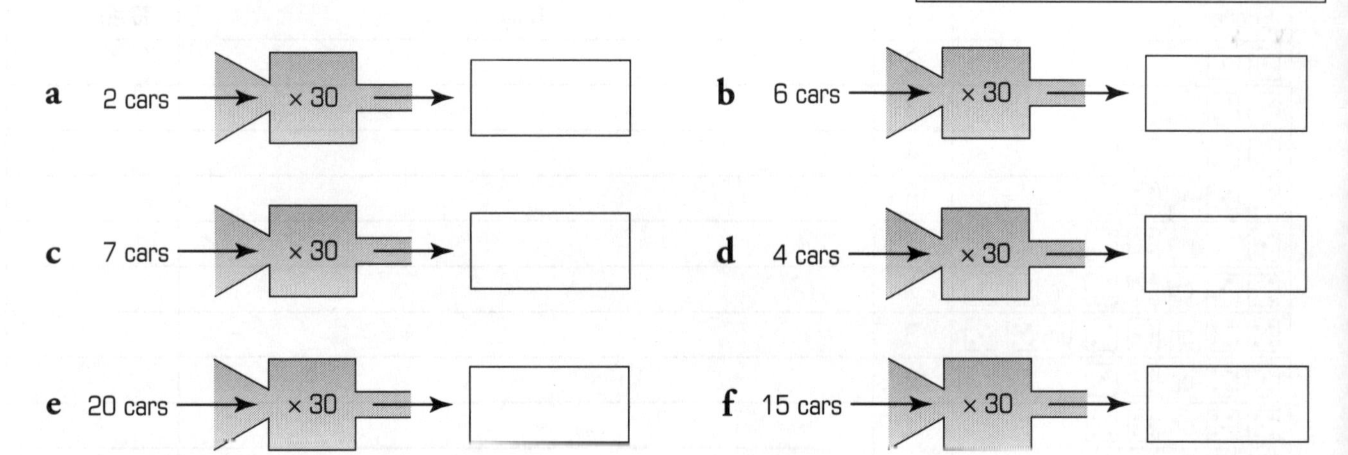

2 Fill in these machines to show Mike's wages when he is paid £50 per car.

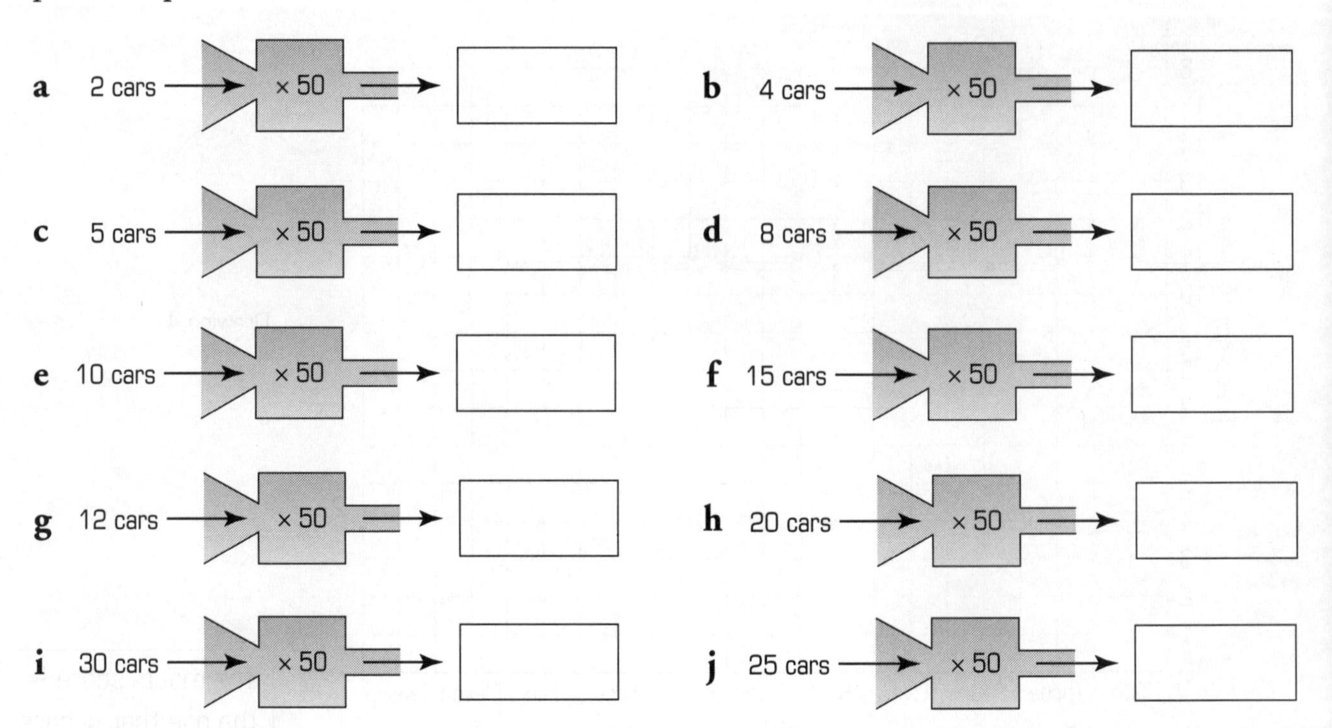

Making sequences

1 This drawing shows 1 table and 5 chairs:

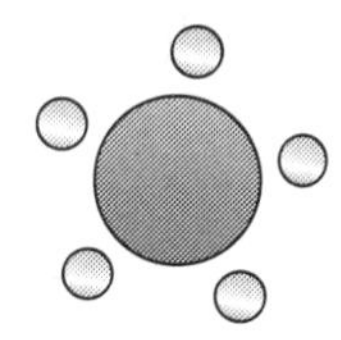

a Complete the third drawing in this sequence:

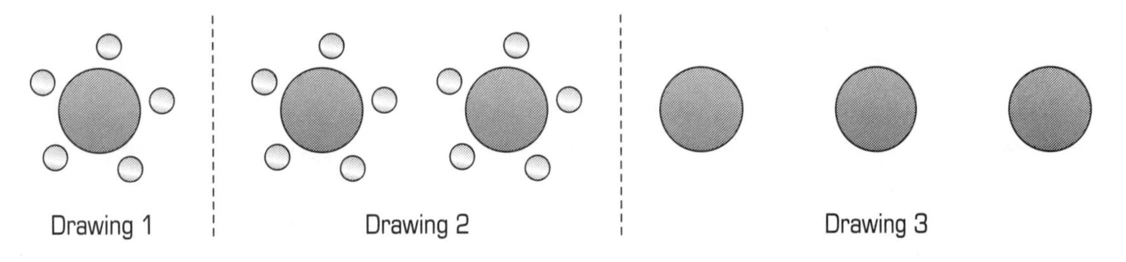

b Complete this sentence: 'Each table has ____ chairs'.

c Write the rule that connects the number of tables and the number of chairs.

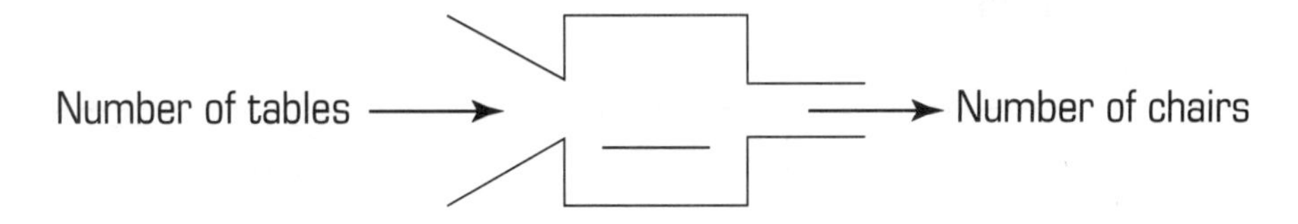

2 a Add the next drawing in this sequence

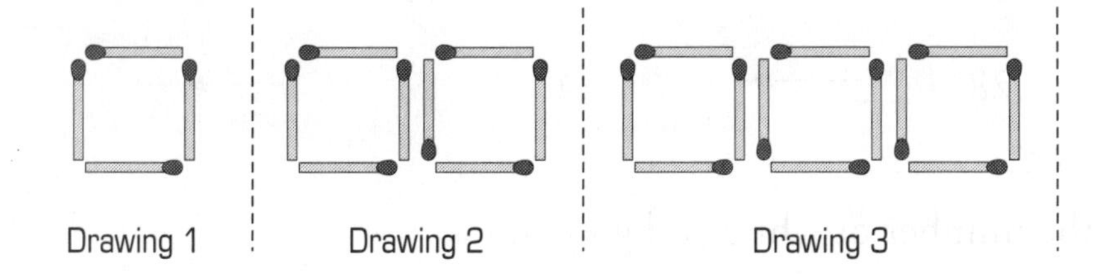

b Complete this sentence: 'Each square uses ____ matches'.

c Write the rule that connects the number of squares and the number of matches.

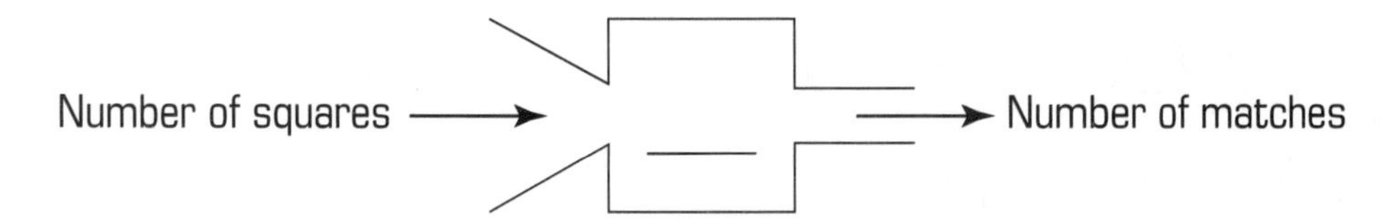

A5.5WS Rules

1 Use the rule in the machine to complete each number mapping.

a

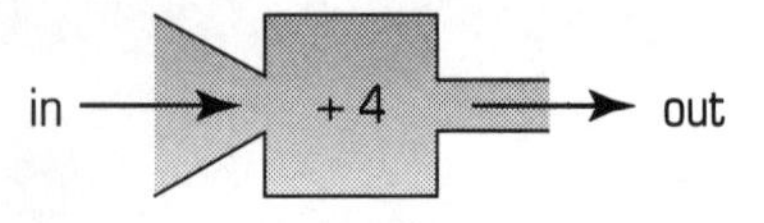

in	→	out
3	→	7
16	→	
32	→	

b

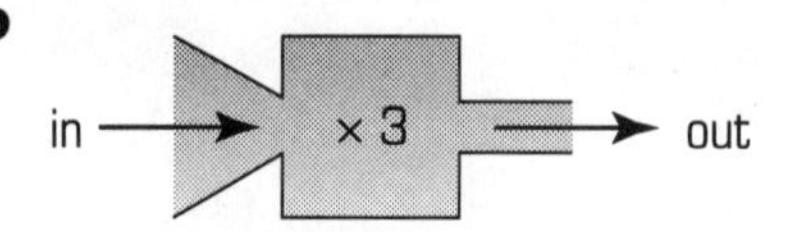

in	→	out
2	→	6
10	→	
30	→	

c

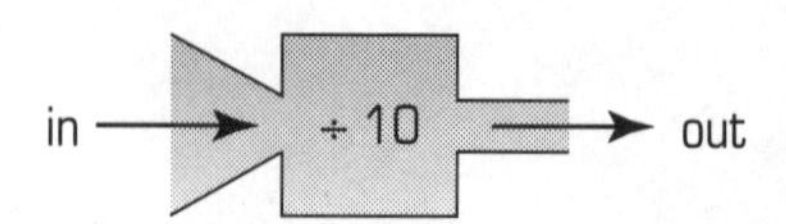

in	→	out
30	→	
50	→	
120	→	

2 For each mapping:

- ▸ Use pairs of values in the mappings to decide on the rule.
- ▸ Write the rule into the machine.
- ▸ Use the rule to complete the mapping.

a

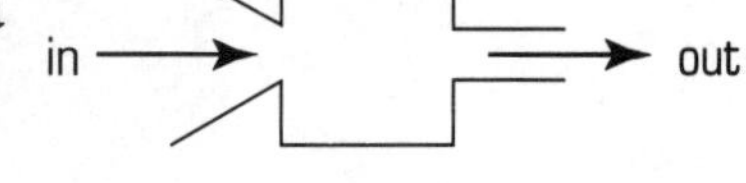

in	→	out
3	→	12
5	→	
10	→	40

b

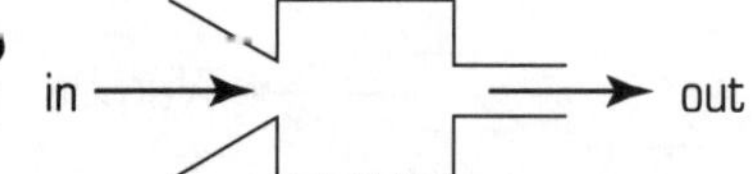

in	→	out
15	→	
10	→	6
28	→	24

c

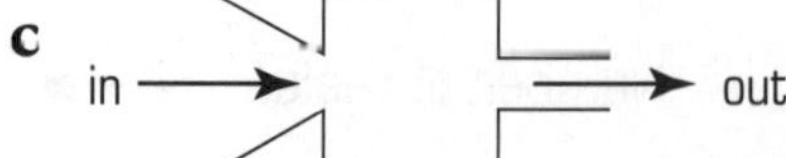

in	→	out
30	→	15
50	→	
12	→	6

3 This is the rule that connects the number of white and grey beads in a necklace.

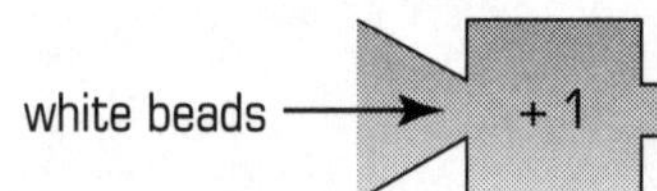

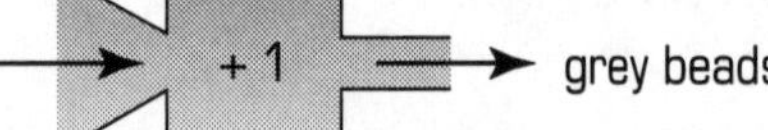

Shade the grey beads on the drawing using the rule.

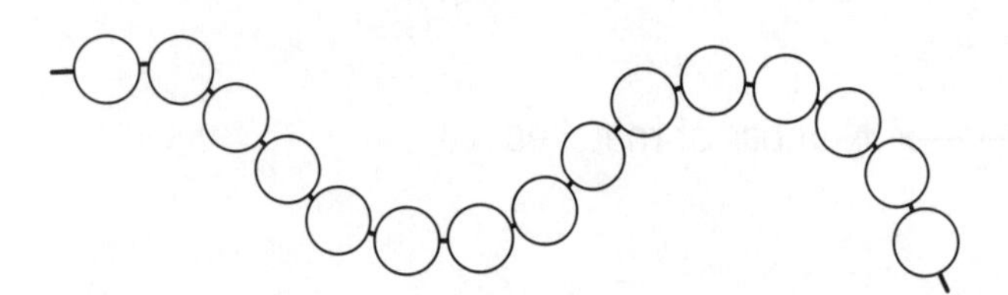

Rules and graphs

1 In this bead pattern there are two black beads for every white bead.

Use the bead pattern to complete this mapping.

black ⟶ **white**

2 ⟶ ☐

4 ⟶ ☐

6 ⟶ ☐

8 ⟶ ☐

2 Write the mapping pairs as graph coordinates.

(2, 1) (4, ____) (6, ____) (8, ____)

3 Plot these coordinates onto this grid.

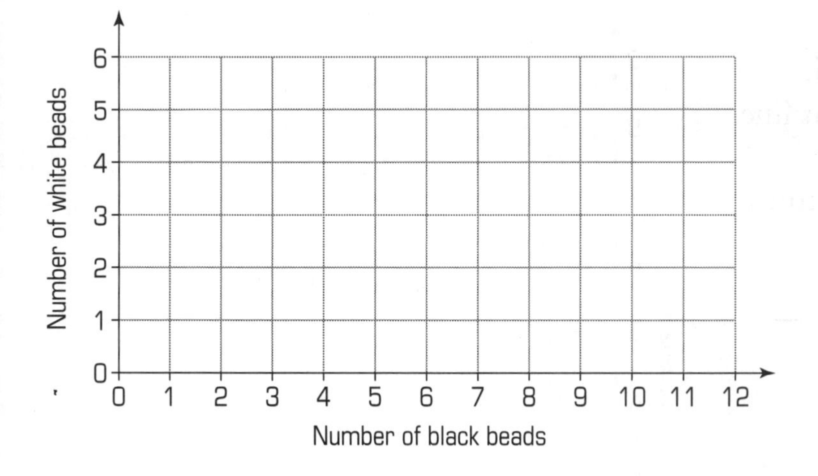

4 Draw a line through the coordinates and extend it as far as you can.

5 Complete these coordinates from the graph.

(10, ____) (____, 6)

A5.7WS Graphs of formulas

The formula for Pete's wage is: $w = n + 3$

w stands for Pete's wage.

n stands for the number of shirts that Pete irons.

1 Use the formula to complete this mapping and the coordinate pairs.

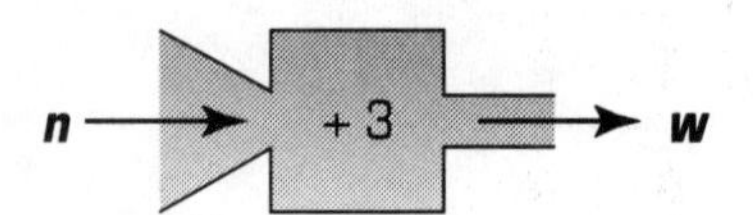

n	→	w	
1	→	4	(1, 4)
2	→	______	(2, ______)
3	→	______	(3, ______)
4	→	______	(______, ______)
5	→	______	(______, ______)

2 Plot the coordinates onto this grid. Join the coordinates with a straight line.

3 How much is Pete paid when he irons 4 shirts?

____

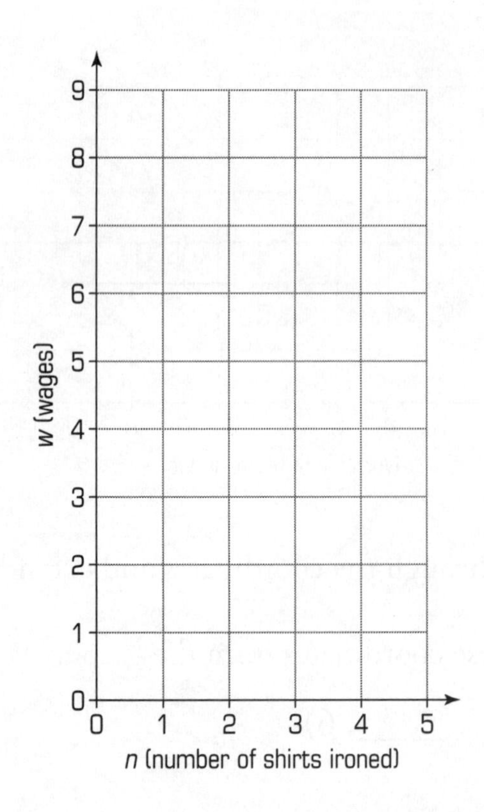

Line symmetry

1 Here are the names of some shapes.
Find and highlight each name in the word search.

OCTAGON
RECTANGLE
TRIANGLE
SQUARE
KITE
POLYGONS
RHOMBUS
PENTAGON
HEXAGON
TRAPEZIUM

G	O	N	R	H	E	C	E	Z	T
P	E	N	H	E	X	A	G	O	N
L	E	P	O	L	Y	G	O	N	S
S	Q	I	M	U	Z	T	O	N	T
X	A	H	B	I	T	E	C	E	R
I	S	Q	U	A	R	E	T	R	A
T	R	A	S	U	I	M	A	E	P
S	R	E	C	T	A	N	G	L	E
T	R	Y	A	A	N	G	O	N	Z
P	E	N	T	A	G	O	N	U	I
R	E	X	E	Z	L	E	T	H	U
F	R	K	I	T	E	L	G	O	M

2 Complete the reflection of these shapes.
Name the completed shapes using the words in question 1.

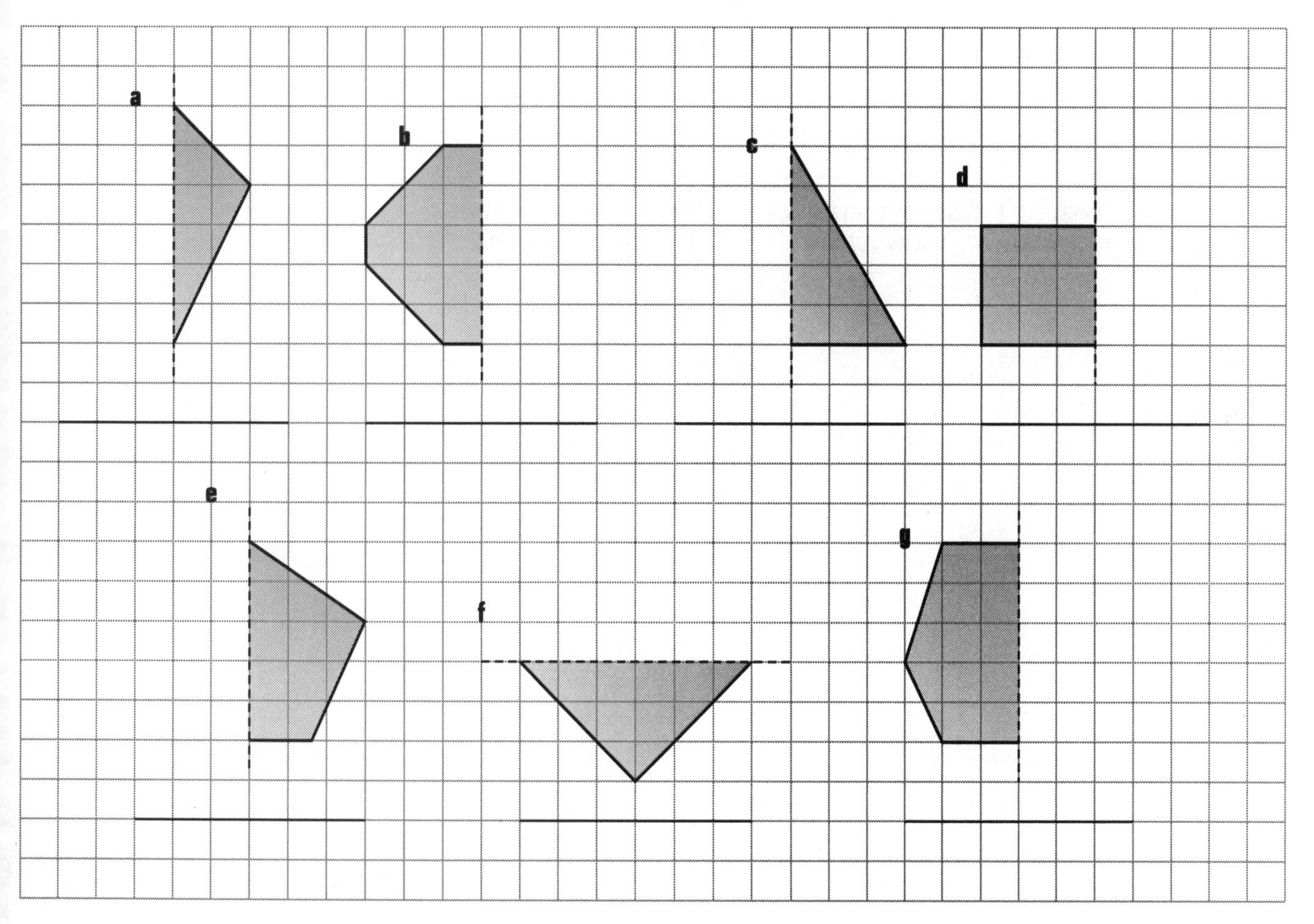

S5.5WS Rotational symmetry

1 Tick (✓) the car number plates that look the same when you turn them up-side-down.
They have rotational symmetry.

96MW96   I85I85   60406   H0I8I0H   XH88HX

2 These shapes can be put into three categories:

- no rotational symmetry
- repeats twice in one rotation
- repeats more than twice in one rotation.

a

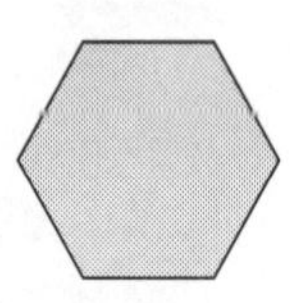

b **c** **d** **e**

f **g** **h** **i** **j**

Put the letter of each shape into the correct column.

No rotational symmetry	Shape repeats twice in one rotation	Shape repeats more than twice in one rotation

3 Which shape in question 2 repeats most times? ______________

4 Draw a shape of your own that has rotational symmetry in the box.

S5.6WS Tessellations

1 Tessellate this shape 15 times on the grid.
It must fit together with no gaps or overlaps.

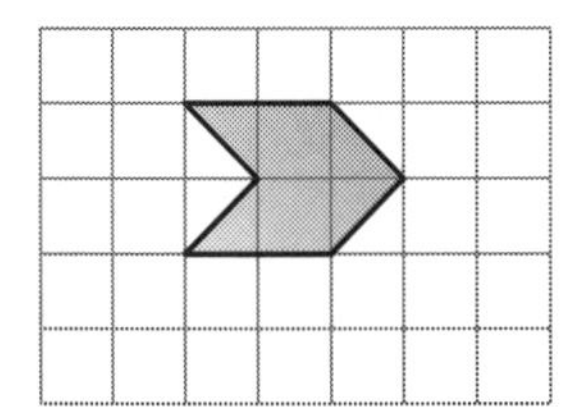

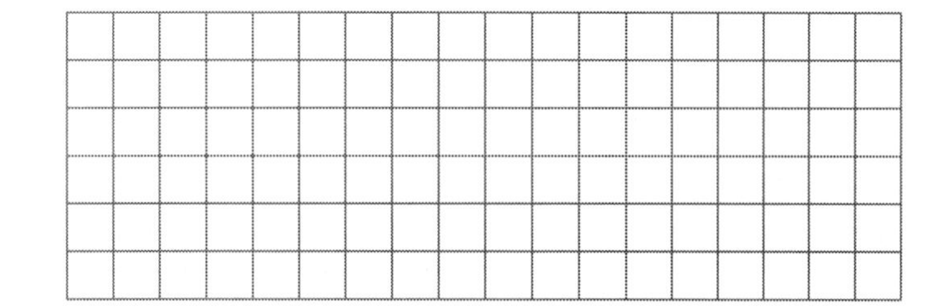

2 Which of these shapes will tessellate? Use the grid to test each shape.
If the shape tessellates, put a tick (✓) inside it.

a

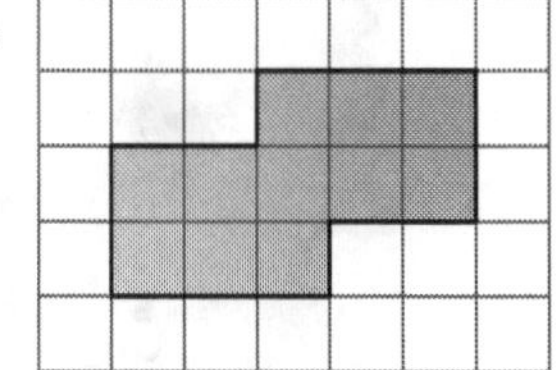

b

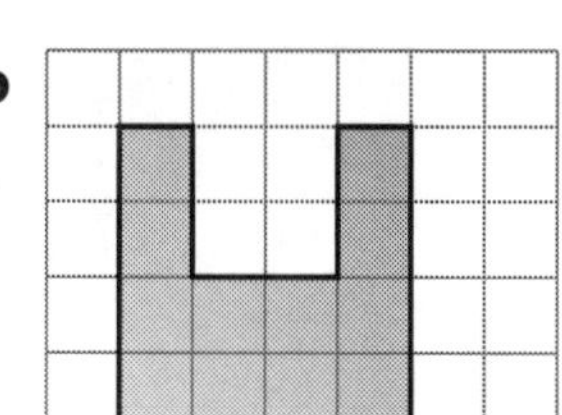

c

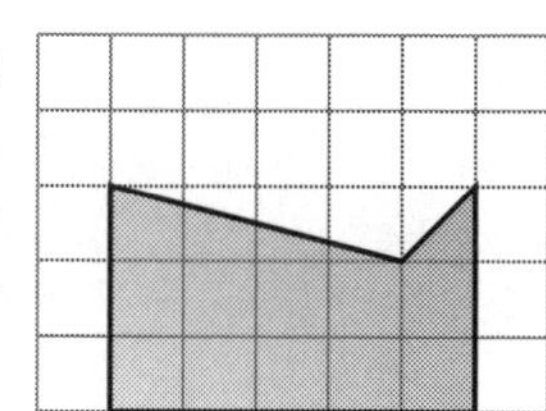

d

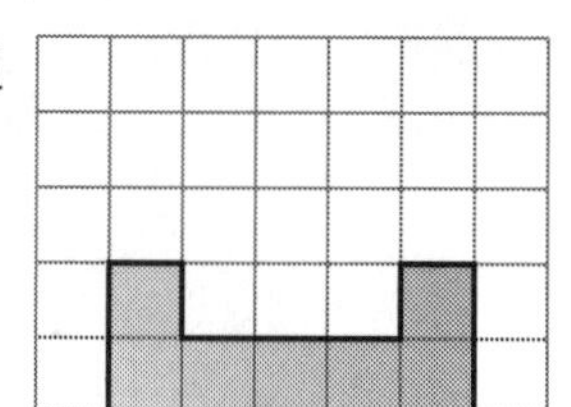

e

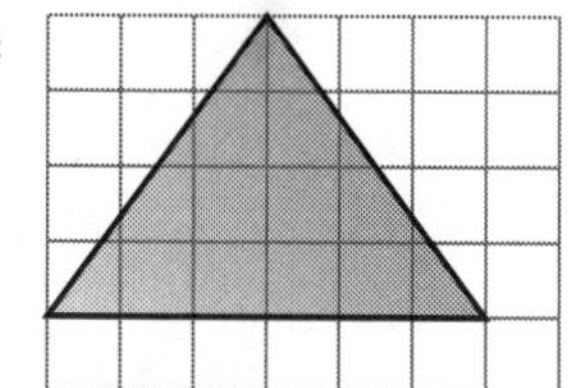

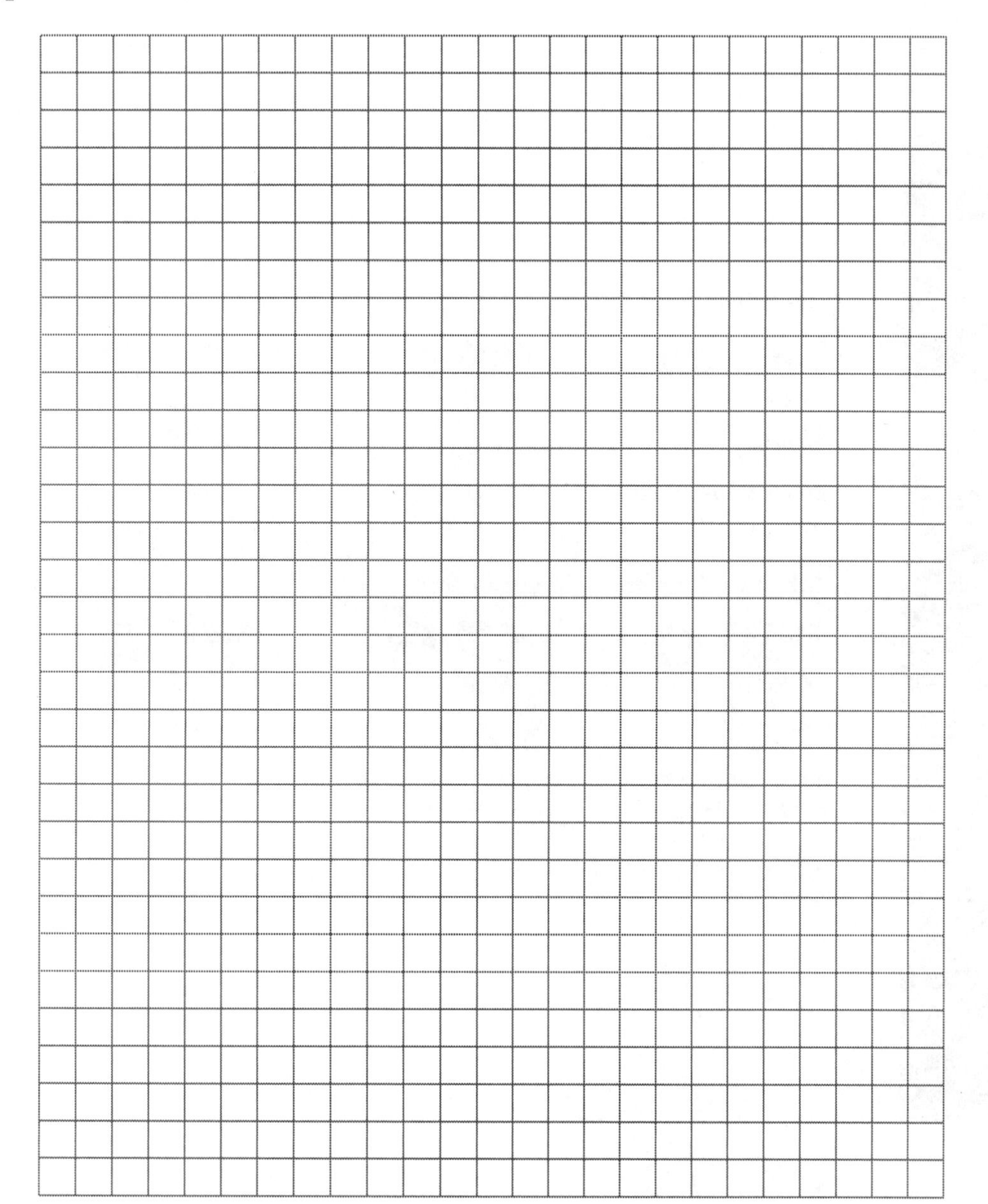

Framework MATHS 7 A

WORKBOOK

Framework Maths is a brand new course designed to match the pitch, pace and progression of the Framework for Teaching Mathematics at Key Stage 3.

The Access tier has been specifically written to help students who find it difficult to access the objectives recommended in the Framework.

This Workbook is written to help consolidate understanding of the key ideas contained in the accompanying Student Book: *Framework Maths 7A*.

The Workbook provides:

- Fill-in tables and charts to save time copying.
- Motivating activities to help reinforce understanding.
- Fully self contained pages that are also suitable for homework.

Framework Maths comprises books for each year of Key Stage 3, at four tiers of ability: Access, Support, Core and Extension.

The full suite of Access materials for year 7 is:

Access Students' Book
ISBN 0 19 914939 9

Access Workbook
ISBN 0 19 914941 0

Access Teacher's Book
ISBN 0 19 914940 2

Other student books in year 7 are:

Core Student's Book
0 19 914849 X

Support Students' Book
ISBN 0 19 914848 1

Extension Students' Book
ISBN 0 19 914847 3

See us on the web at: **www.OxfordSecondary.co.uk**

OXFORD
UNIVERSITY PRESS

Orders and enquiries to Customer Services:
tel. 01536 741068
fax 01536 454519

www.oup.com